Introduction to

CONTEMPORARY MATHEMATICS

[signature] 1980

HOLDEN–DAY SERIES IN MATHEMATICS
Earl E. Coddington and Andrew M. Gleason, Editors

G. HOCHSCHILD, *The Structure of Lie Groups*
SZE–TSEN HU, *Elements of General Topology*
SZE–TSEN HU, *Elements of Modern Algebra*
SZE–TSEN HU, *Introduction to Contemporary Mathematics*

Introduction to
CONTEMPORARY MATHEMATICS

Sze-Tsen Hu

Department of Mathematics
University of California, Los Angeles

HOLDEN–DAY, INC.
San Francisco, London, Amsterdam
1966

PREFACE

The origin of the present book was a set of lecture notes at Wayne State University, designed for the first fundamental course for mathematics majors after two years of calculus. The objective of the course was to give the beginning majors a brief guided tour through various branches of contemporary mathematics, emphasizing the austere aspect of abstraction and precision without becoming involved in the complications of deeper results.

Apart from its main use for a course as described above, this book could be used as a text for a stimulating teachers training course at the upper division level or for summer institutes of high school teachers. The chapters are only loosely related and hence can be used separately as texts for various short training courses.

Since knowledge of calculus is not necessary, this book could be used as a first-year course in mathematics for those college students who do not feel bound or inclined to study calculus. Besides, it could be assigned as a challenging reference book for the bright students of calculus courses.

The manuscript of the present book was tested by the author in the spring semester of 1965 at UCLA with exciting success in a very heterogeneous class of about forty students. More than one half of the class were nonmathematicians; they were upper division undergraduates or graduate students in the humanities, life sciences, education, and engineering departments. Many of them had not taken any calculus courses. The students seemed to enjoy a precise presentation of easier materials much more than vague intuitive descriptions of deeper results.

Cross references are given in the form (IV, 5.8), where IV stands for Chapter IV and 5.8 for the numbering of the statement in the chapter. The chapter numeral will be omitted in case the reference is made in the same chapter.

A list of special symbols and abbreviations used in this book is given immediately after the Table of Contents. Certain deviations from standard set-theoretic notations have been adopted in the text; namely, □ is

v

used to denote the empty set and $A \setminus B$ the set-theoretic difference usually denoted by $A - B$. We have used the symbol $\parallel$ to indicate the end of a proof, and the abbreviation "iff" for the phrase "if and only if."

The author acknowledges with great pleasure his gratitude to Professor Martin T. Wechsler of Wayne State University for his suggestions made in 1959 which improved the lecture notes mentioned above. Finally, it is a pleasure to thank the publisher and the printer for their courtesy and cooperation.

Sze-Tsen Hu

University of California
Los Angeles, Calif.

TABLE OF CONTENTS

Chapter V: ELEMENTARY TOPOLOGY

Chapter I: SETS AND FUNCTIONS

In this leading chapter of the book, we will give an elementary account of sets, functions, relations, and cardinal numbers, with the primary purpose of introducing the terminology and the notation to be used in the sequel.

1. LOGICAL PRELIMINARIES

By a *statement*, we mean a complete sentence which makes sense. Examples of statements are as follows:

(1) The sun rises from the east.
(2) This desk is made of gold.
(3) Dogs have four legs.
(4) Two distinct points determine a line.
(5) Seven is a prime number.

The important feature of a statement is that it must be meaningful to call it "true" or "false." Statements which have been proved to be true are usually called *propositions, theorems, lemmas, corollaries,* etc. A statement may be denoted by any kind of symbols, say for example, p, q, ...

If one asserts a statement without qualification, then it is understood that he claims that his statement is true. To claim that a given statement is false, one may do so by adding the phrase "it is false that" in front of the statement or by using some negative word such as "not." The statement obtained in this way is called the *negation* of the given statement. For example, the negations of statements (1)–(5) are as follows:

($\tilde{1}$) The sun does *not* rise from the east. = *It is false that* the sun rises from the east.

($\tilde{2}$) This desk is *not* made of gold.

($\tilde{3}$) *It is false that* dogs have four legs.

($\tilde{4}$) *It is false that* two distinct points determine a line.

($\tilde{5}$) Seven is *not* a prime number.

There are many ways of combining statements, all of which are derived from three fundamental operations:

Conjunction. Here one claims the *simultaneous* truth of two statements. *Example.* Dogs have four legs *and* birds have two legs.

Disjunction. Here one claims the truth of *at least one* of two statements. *Example.* It will be raining tonight *or* it will be raining tomorrow.

We emphasize that "or" means "*at least one*" of the statements is true and does not mean "*one and only one*" of the statements is true.

Implication. Usually implication takes the form "If p, then q." Here, one claims that "p is false or q is true."
Example. If it will be raining, then I shall stay at home.

For the implication "If p, then q," we shall adopt the symbol

$$p \Rightarrow q$$

which reads "p *implies* q."

If $p \Rightarrow q$ is true, then p is called a *sufficient condition* for q and q is called a *necessary condition* for p.

The implication $q \Rightarrow p$ is called the *converse* of $p \Rightarrow q$.

If $p \Rightarrow q$ and its converse $q \Rightarrow p$ are both true, we say that p and q are *equivalent;* in symbols, $p \Leftrightarrow q$. In this case, p is called a *necessary and sufficient condition* for q, and vice versa. Sometimes, an equivalence is expressed by the phrase "if and only if." We shall use a special abbreviation for this phrase of frequent occurrence: "iff."

The negations of combined statements have the following properties:

(1.1) *The negation of a conjunction is equivalent to the disjunction of the negations.* Precisely, the statement "It is false that p and q" is equivalent to the statement "p is false or q is false."

(1.2) *The negation of a disjunction is equivalent to the conjunction of the negations.* Precisely, the statement "It is false that p or q" is equivalent to the statement "p is false and q is false."

(1.3) *The negation of the implication $p \Rightarrow q$ is equivalent to the statement* "p is true and q is false."

EXERCISES

1A. Find the negations of the following statements:
  (a) Mr. Smith is a teacher.
  (b) Eleven is a prime number.

(c) This work was done either by John or by Jean.

(d) Neither Mary nor Frank has completed the assignment.

1B. Write the following implications explicitly in the form "If p, then q":

(a) I stay at home on rainy days.

(b) The square of a nonzero real number is positive.

(c) The base angles of an isosceles triangle are equal.

1C. Find the negations of the implications obtained in Exercise 1B.

1D. Find the converses of the implications obtained in Exercise 1B.

2. THE IDEA OF A SET

To understand any branch of knowledge, one has to know the precise meaning of the words used in the statements. In school, you were taught to look up their definitions in a dictionary. If you do so, you will find a statement of the meaning of the new word in terms of some other words. If you look up these new words, you will find that they are defined by means of still more words. If you carry on this process indefinitely, sooner or later you will find yourself going in circles. Since circular definitions are not allowed in mathematics, we have to take a small number of words *undefined*. One of the undefined terms in mathematics is the word "set."

By a *set*, we mean any collection of objects. This is not a mathematical definition because the word "collection" is merely a synonym of the word "set." The student is expected to be able to understand the intuitive meaning of this undefined term. In the text, we will occasionally use other synonyms of the word "set," namely, "aggregate," "family," etc.

EXAMPLES OF SETS

(1) The student body of UCLA (i.e., the set of all students of UCLA)

(2) The set of all citizens of the United States of America

(3) The set of the names of the days in a week, namely, Sunday, Monday, Tuesday, Wednesday, Thursday, Friday, and Saturday

(4) The set N of all natural numbers, i.e., positive integers

(5) The set Z of all integers, positive, negative, or zero

(6) The set Q of all rational numbers

(7) The set R of all real numbers

(8) The set C of all complex numbers

(9) The set I of all real numbers x satisfying the condition $0 \leqslant x \leqslant 1$; this set I will be called *the unit interval*.

(10) The set of all roots (real or imaginary) of the equation $x^3 + px + q = 0$.

The objects in a given set S are called the *members*, the *elements*, or the *points* of S. These may be concrete things as in Example (1) or abstract notions as in Example (9). We shall use the symbol ϵ for the phrase "is a member of." Thus, the notation

$$x \in S$$

reads "x is member of S." Equivalently, it can be read as "x belongs to S" or simply as "x is in S." The negation of $x \in S$ will be denoted by

$$x \notin S$$

and reads "x is not a member of S."

To determine a set S, one has to determine its members. Precisely, a set S is said to be *determined* iff one can tell whether or not any given object x belongs to S.

In Example (1), the registrar of UCLA can determine by his record whether a given object is a student of UCLA. In Example (2), the Justice Department or, if necessary, the Supreme Court of the U.S.A. will be able to decide if a given object is a citizen of the U.S.A.

Let us give an example where a set is not well-defined. Mr. John Jones is a barber. One day, he asserted: "I shave every man who does not shave himself and no others." Our question is whether or not the persons whom Mr. John Jones shaves form a set. The answer is negative. The crucial point is that we cannot determine whether or not Mr. John Jones shaves himself. This example shows that the *totality of sets each of which does not contain itself as a member does not form a set.*

Frequently, the members of a set S are determined by the possession of a certain property. For example, if $p(x)$ stands for an arbitrarily given statement relating to the object x, then we write

$$S = \{x \mid p(x)\}$$

to state that S is the set of all objects x for which the statement $p(x)$ is true. This set S is called the *set defined by the statement $p(x)$.*

In Example (1), the student body of UCLA is defined by the statement that "x is a student of UCLA."

A set S is said to be *empty* (or *vacuous*) iff it has no member. There is precisely one empty set which will be denoted by the symbol $\square$. Therefore, the notation

$$S = \square$$

reads "S is empty." On the other hand, the notation

$$S \neq \square$$

reads "S is nonempty." Hence, $S \neq \square$ iff S contains at least one member.

A set S is called a *singleton* iff it contains one and only one member. If the lone member of a singleton S is x, then we shall denote it by

$$S = \{x\}.$$

More generally, if $x_1, x_2, \ldots, x_n$ are n arbitrarily given objects, then

$$S = \{x_1, x_2, \ldots, x_n\}$$

denotes the set S which consists of the objects $x_1, x_2, \ldots, x_n$ as members.

EXERCISES

2A. Examine whether each of the following phrases defines a set:
    (a) The present senators of the U.S.A.
    (b) The past senators of the U.S.A.
    (c) The future senators of the U.S.A.

2B. Determine the members of the following sets:
    (a) The set of all living ex-presidents of the U.S.A.
    (b) The set of all natural numbers x satisfying $3x - 4 = 2$
    (c) The set of all integers x with $x^2 = 4$
    (d) The set of all acute angles θ with $\sin \theta = \frac{1}{2}$.

2C. Prove that each of the following sets is the empty set:
    (a) The set of all female ex-presidents of the U.S.A.
    (b) The set of all real numbers x satisfying $x^2 + 1 = 0$
    (c) The set of all integers x with $2x = 1$
    (d) The set of all acute angles θ with $\sin \theta = 2$.

3. SUBSETS AND QUANTIFIERS

Let A and B denote any two given sets. In case every member of A belongs to B, we say that A *is contained in* B, or equivalently, B *contains* A. In symbols, we have

$$A \subset B, \qquad B \supset A.$$

Therefore, $A \subset B$ iff $x \in A$ implies $x \in B$. This symbol $\subset$ is called the *inclusion*.

For example, the unit interval I in Example (9) of §2 is contained in the set R of all real numbers. Also, we have

$$N \subset \mathcal{Z} \subset Q \subset R \subset C$$

in Examples (4)–(8) of §2.

If $A \subset B$, then we say that A is a *subset* of B. If $A \subset B$ and $B \subset A$ are both true, then the sets A and B are said to be *equal;* in symbols,

$$A = B.$$

Therefore, two sets are equal iff they have precisely the same members. If $A \subset B$ and $A \neq B$, then we say that A is a *proper subset* of B. A proper subset A of a set B is illustrated by the following figure.

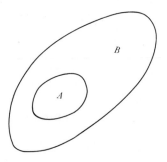

Figure 1

The subsets of a given set S are frequently defined by imposing further statements, called *conditions,* on the members of S. For example, let $p(x)$ denote a given statement relating to the member x of S. Then

$$\{x \in S \mid p(x)\}$$

stands for the subset of S which consists of all members $x \in S$ such that $p(x)$ is true. In this case, the statement $p(x)$ is called the *defining condition* of the subset. Thus, the unit interval I is a subset of the set R of all real numbers defined by the condition $0 \leqslant x \leqslant 1$, i.e.,

$$I = \{x \in R \mid 0 \leqslant x \leqslant 1\}.$$

Suppose that S is an arbitrarily given set and that we want to make statements about portions of this set S. In doing so, we use such words as "all," "some," etc., to indicate how many members of the set S are involved. These words are called *quantifiers.*

For example, let S denote the set of all living men on the earth. Statements like

(a) All men are mortal.

(b) Some men are teachers.

refer to portions of the set S by means of the quantifiers "all" and "some."

Let x denote an arbitrary member of the set S, i.e., any living man

on the earth, and let $p(x)$ stand for the statement "x is mortal." Then
(**a**) can be restated in the form of the following statement:

(**a'**) $p(x)$ for every $x \in S$.

Thus the quantifiers "all," "each," and "every" have the same mathematical meaning, often denoted by the symbol V.

On the other hand, let $q(x)$ stand for the statement "x is a teacher." Then (**b**) can be restated in the form of the following statement:

(**b'**) $q(x)$ for some $x \in S$.

This quantifier "some" has an equivalent form: "there exists a." Precisely, (**b'**) is equivalent to the following statement:

(**b''**) There exists an $x \in S$ such that $q(x)$.

Occasionally, the symbol $\mathcal{J}$ will be used to stand for the phrase "there exists a."

One can explain the meaning of the quantifiers "all" and "some" by means of the subsets defined by the statements. For this purpose, let

$$A = \{x \in S \mid p(x)\},$$
$$B = \{x \in S \mid q(x)\}.$$

Then we have the following obvious propositions:

(3.1) $p(x)$ for all $x \in S$ iff $A = S$;
(3.2) $q(x)$ for some $x \in S$ iff $B \neq \square$.

Finally, the negations of statements (**a'**) and (**b'**) are the following statements $(\tilde{\mathbf{a}})$ and $(\tilde{\mathbf{b}})$ respectively:

$(\tilde{\mathbf{a}})$ $p(x)$ is false for some $x \in S$.
$(\tilde{\mathbf{b}})$ $q(x)$ is false for all $x \in S$.

Note the interchange of the quantifiers "all" and "some" in the negations.

EXERCISES

3A. Determine the members of the following subsets of the set R of all real numbers:

(a) $\{x \in R \mid x^2 = 1\}$
(b) $\{x \in R \mid x^2 - 3x + 2 = 0\}$
(c) $\{x \in R \mid x^3 = 1\}$
(d) $\{x \in R \mid 2^x = 1\}$.

3B. Find obvious inclusions among the following subsets of the student body X of UCLA:
- (a) The subset A of X which consists of all students having at least one advanced degree in mathematics
- (b) The subset C of X which consists of candidates for the Ph.D. in mathematics
- (c) The subset G of X which consists of graduate students in mathematics
- (d) The subset M of X which consists of all students who have had at least one course in mathematics.

3C. Find all possible inclusions among the following subsets of the set R of all real numbers:
- (a) The subset P of all positive real numbers
- (b) The (closed) unit interval $I = [0, 1]$ which consists of all real numbers x satisfying $0 \leqslant x \leqslant 1$
- (c) The interval $(0, 1]$ which consists of all real numbers x satisfying $0 < x \leqslant 1$
- (d) The interval $[0, 1)$ which consists of all real numbers x satisfying $0 \leqslant x < 1$
- (e) The open unit interval $(0, 1)$ which consists of all real numbers x satisfying $0 < x < 1$
- (f) The set N of all natural numbers.

3D. Write down all subsets of the set $S = \{1, 2, 3\}$.

4. ALGEBRA OF SETS

There are various ways leading to the formation of new sets from old ones. In particular, we have the following three fundamental operations.

Union. For any two given sets A and B, their *union* $A \cup B$ is defined to be the set which consists of those objects x which belong to at least one of the sets A and B. In symbols, we have

$$A \cup B = \{x \mid x \in A \quad \text{or} \quad x \in B\}.$$

Therefore, union and disjunction are closely related; in fact, for an arbitrary object x, we have the following equivalence:

$$x \in A \cup B \Leftrightarrow x \in A \quad \text{or} \quad x \in B.$$

EXAMPLES OF UNIONS

(U1) The American Mathematical Society, abbreviated AMS, and the Mathematical Association of America, abbreviated MAA, held a joint annual meeting and it happened that all members of the two organizations attended. Then the persons who attended the meeting form the union of AMS and MAA; i.e.,

$$\text{AMS} \cup \text{MAA}.$$

(U2) Let A and B denote the following sets of natural numbers:

$$A = \{1, 2, 3, 4\}$$
$$B = \{3, 4, 5\}.$$

Then their union $A \cup B$ is the following set

$$A \cup B = \{1, 2, 3, 4, 5\}.$$

The union $A \cup B$ of two sets A and B can be represented by the shaded area of the following figure.

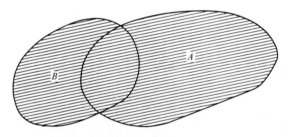

FIGURE 2

Intersection. For any two given sets A and B, their *intersection* $A \cap B$ is defined to be the set of all common members of A and B. In symbols, we have

$$A \cap B = \{x \mid x \in A \quad \text{and} \quad x \in B\}.$$

Therefore, intersection and conjunction are closely related; in fact, for an arbitrarily given object x, we have the following equivalence:

$$x \in A \cap B \Leftrightarrow x \in A \quad \text{and} \quad x \in B.$$

EXAMPLES OF INTERSECTIONS

(I1) In example **(U1)**, the intersection

$$\text{AMS} \cap \text{MAA}$$

is the set of all persons who are members of both AMS and MAA.

(I2) In example **(U2)**, the intersection $A \cap B$ is the following set:

$$A \cap B = \{3, 4\}.$$

(I3) The intersection $Z \cap I$ of the set Z of all integers and the unit interval I of real numbers is the following set

$$Z \cap I = \{0, 1\}.$$

The intersection $A \cap B$ of two sets A and B can be represented by the shaded area of the following figure.

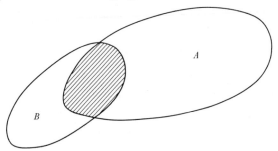

FIGURE 3

Difference. For any two given sets A and B, the *(set-theoretic) difference* $A \setminus B$ is defined to be the set of all objects which are members of A but not members of B. In symbols, we have

$$A \setminus B = \{x \mid x \in A \quad \text{and} \quad x \notin B\}.$$

Therefore, for an arbitrarily given object x, we have the following equivalence:

$$x \in A \setminus B \Leftrightarrow x \in A \quad \text{and} \quad x \notin B.$$

EXAMPLES OF DIFFERENCES

(D1) In example **(U1)** the difference

$$\text{AMS} \setminus \text{MAA}$$

is the set of all persons who are members of AMS but not members of MAA.

(D2) In example **(U2)**, the difference $A \setminus B$ is the following set:

$$A \setminus B = \{1, 2\}.$$

The difference $A \setminus B$ of two sets A and B can be represented by the shaded area of the following figure.

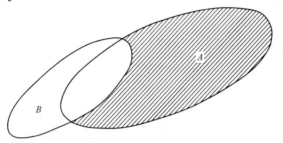

FIGURE 4

Two sets A and B are said to be *disjoint* iff $A \cap B = \square$; otherwise, they are said to be *overlapping*. Thus, A and B are disjoint iff $A \backslash B = A$.

THEOREM 4.1. *Let A, B, C, and X be arbitrarily given sets. Then the following statements are true:*

(1) *Commutative laws:*

$$A \cup B = B \cup A$$
$$A \cap B = B \cap A$$

(2) *Associative laws:*

$$A \cup (B \cup C) = (A \cup B) \cup C$$
$$A \cap (B \cap C) = (A \cap B) \cap C$$

(3) *Distributive laws:*

$$A \cap (B \cup C) = (A \cap B) \cup (A \cap C)$$
$$A \cup (B \cap C) = (A \cup B) \cap (A \cup C)$$

(4) $X \backslash (X \backslash A) = A \cap X$

(5) *De Morgan formulae:*

$$X \backslash (A \cup B) = (X \backslash A) \cap (X \backslash B)$$
$$X \backslash (A \cap B) = (X \backslash A) \cup (X \backslash B).$$

Proof. (1) and (2) are obvious, by the definition of union and intersection.

To establish (3), let x be an arbitrary member of the set $A \cap (B \cup C)$. By the definition of intersection, we have $x \in A$ and $x \in B \cup C$. By the definition of union, $x \in B \cup C$ implies that $x \in B$ or $x \in C$. In case $x \in B$, we have $x \in A$ and $x \in B$; therefore, we get $x \in A \cap B$. In case $x \in C$, we have $x \in A$ and $x \in C$; therefore, we get $x \in A \cap C$. Since at least one of these two cases must be true, it follows that $x \in (A \cap B) \cup (A \cap C)$.

Since x is any member of $A \cap (B \cup C)$, we have proved the following inclusion:

(i) $\qquad\qquad A \cap (B \cup C) \subset (A \cap B) \cup (A \cap C).$

On the other hand, let x be an arbitrary member of $(A \cap B) \cup (A \cap C)$. Then it follows that $x \in A \cap B$ or $x \in A \cap C$. In case $x \in A \cap B$, we have $x \in A$ and $x \in B$. In case $x \in A \cap C$, we have $x \in A$ and $x \in C$. Therefore, we always have $x \in A$. Besides, we have $x \in B$ or $x \in C$. Hence, $x \in A$ and $x \in B \cup C$. This implies that $x \in A \cap (B \cup C)$. Since x is any member of $(A \cap B) \cup (A \cap C)$, we have proved the following inclusion:

(ii) $\qquad\qquad A \cap (B \cup C) \supset (A \cap B) \cup (A \cap C).$

Because of inclusions **(i)** and **(ii)**, we have established the equality

$$A \cap (B \cup C) = (A \cap B) \cup (A \cap C).$$

Similarly, one can establish the second equality in **(3)**.

To establish **(4)**, let x be an arbitrary member of $X \backslash (X \backslash A)$. By the definition of difference, we have $x \in X$ and $x \notin X \backslash A$. This implies $x \in A$. Hence we have $x \in A \cap X$. Since x is any member of $X \backslash (X \backslash A)$, we have proved the following inclusion:

(iii) $\qquad\qquad X \backslash (X \backslash A) \subset A \cap X.$

On the other hand, let x be an arbitrary member of $A \cap X$. Then we have $x \in A$ and $x \in X$. Since $x \in A$, we get $x \notin X \backslash A$. Thus, $x \in X \backslash (X \backslash A)$. Since x is any member of $A \cap X$, we have proved the following inclusion:

(iv) $\qquad\qquad X \backslash (X \backslash A) \supset A \cap X.$

Inclusions **(iii)** and **(iv)** imply the equality **(4)**.

To establish **(5)**, let x be an arbitrary member of $X \backslash (A \cup B)$. Then we have $x \in X$ and $x \notin A \cup B$. Since $x \notin A \cup B$, it follows that $x \notin A$ and $x \notin B$. Since $x \in X$ and $x \notin A$, we have $x \in X \backslash A$. Similarly, we also have $x \in X \backslash B$. Hence, $x \in (X \backslash A) \cap (X \backslash B)$. Since x is any member of $X \backslash (A \cup B)$, we have proved the following inclusion:

(v) $\qquad\qquad X \backslash (A \cup B) \subset (X \backslash A) \cap (X \backslash B).$

On the other hand, let x be an arbitrary member of $(X \backslash A) \cap (X \backslash B)$. Then $x \in X \backslash A$ and $x \in X \backslash B$. Since $x \in X \backslash A$, we have $x \in X$ and $x \notin A$. Since $x \in X \backslash B$, we also have $x \notin B$. Hence, $x \in X$ and $x \notin A \cup B$. This implies that $x \in X \backslash (A \cup B)$. Since x is any member of $(X \backslash A) \cap (X \backslash B)$, we have proved the following inclusion:

(vi) $\qquad\qquad X \backslash (A \cup B) \supset (X \backslash A) \cap (X \backslash B).$

Inclusions (**v**) and (**vi**) imply the first equality in (**5**). Similarly, one can establish the second equality in (**5**).‖

Let X be an arbitrarily given set and consider the subsets of X. The totality of the subsets of X forms a set which will be denoted by the symbol

$$2^X.$$

This notation will be explained in the next section. The subsets of X are the members of 2^X.

For every set $A \in 2^X$, the set $X \backslash A$ is called the *complement* of A in X. We usually omit the phrase "in X" if it is obvious in the context. Sometimes, we will also use the notation

$$\tilde{A} = X \backslash A.$$

Thus, in the set 2^X, we have defined the operations

$$A \cup B, \qquad A \cap B, \qquad \tilde{A}$$

satisfying Conditions (**1**)–(**5**) in (**4.1**). This is an example of Boolean algebra which will be defined in a later chapter.

EXERCISES

4A. Prove the second equality in (3) of Theorem 4.1 and the second equality of (5) of the same.

4B. Establish the following relations for arbitrary sets X and Y:
   (a) $\square \subset X$
   (b) $X \subset X$
   (c) $X \cup \square = X$
   (d) $X \cap \square = \square$
   (e) $X \cap X = X = X \cup X$
   (f) $X \cap Y \subset X \subset X \cup Y$.

4C. Prove the following statements for arbitrary sets X, Y, and Z:
   (a) If $X \subset Y$ and $Y \subset Z$, then $X \subset Z$
   (b) If $X \subset Z$ and $Y \subset Z$, then $X \cup Y \subset Z$
   (c) If $X \supset Z$ and $Y \supset Z$, then $X \cap Y \supset Z$.

4D. Let A and B be arbitrary subsets of a set X. Prove that the following statements are equivalent:
   (a) $A \subset B$
   (b) $A \cap B = A$

(c) $A \cup B = B$

(d) $X \backslash B \subset X \backslash A$

(e) $A \cap (X \backslash B) = \square$

(f) $(X \backslash A) \cup B = X.$

4E. Verify the following properties of subsets of a given set X:

(a) $\tilde{X} = \square$

(b) $\tilde{\square} = X$

(c) $A \cup \tilde{A} = X$

(d) $A \cap \tilde{A} = \square$

(e) $X \backslash \tilde{A} = A$

(f) $X \backslash (A \cup B) = \tilde{A} \cap \tilde{B}$

(g) $X \backslash (A \cap B) = \tilde{A} \cap \tilde{B}$

(h) $X \backslash (A \backslash B) = B \cup \tilde{A}$

(i) If $A \cap B = \square$ and $A \cup B = \square$, then $\tilde{A} = B$

(j) If $A \subset B$, then $\tilde{A} \supset \tilde{B}.$

5. THE IDEA OF A FUNCTION

Let X denote the set of all students in a class and Y denote the set of all possible family names. In making the roll of the class X, every student gave the professor his family name. In this way, we have performed an operation f, which assigns to each student $x \in X$ his family name, $f(x) \in Y$. Such an operation is called a function from X into Y.

In general, let X and Y be arbitrarily given sets. By a *function*

$$f : X \rightarrow Y$$

from X into Y, we mean an operation which assigns to each member $x \in X$ a member $f(x) \in Y$.

EXAMPLES OF FUNCTIONS

(1) Let X denote the set of all students in a class and let Y denote the set of all possible grades, i.e.

$$Y = \{A, B, C, D, F\}.$$

The result of the midsemester test will establish an operation which assigns to each student $x \in X$ his grade $f(x) \in Y$ in the test. This operation $x \rightarrow f(x)$ defines a function

$$f : X \rightarrow Y.$$

(2) Let us consider the set N of all natural numbers and the set Z_p of all nonnegative integers less than a given positive integer $p > 1$. For each $x \in N$, let us divide x by p and obtain a remainder $f(x)$. This number $f(x)$ is obviously in the set Z_p. The operation $x \rightarrow f(x)$ defines a function

$$f:N \rightarrow Z_p.$$

(3) Let us consider the equation $y = x^2$. For an arbitrary real number x, $y = x^2$ is also a real number. Hence the operation $x \rightarrow x^2$ defines a function

$$f:R \rightarrow R.$$

This function is usually denoted by x^2. Hence we have

$$x^2:R \rightarrow R.$$

Now let us consider an arbitrarily given function

$$f:X \rightarrow Y$$

from a set X into a set Y.

The set X will be called the *domain* of the function f, and the set Y will be referred to as the *range* of the function f.

For an arbitrary point x of the domain X of f, the point $f(x)$ of Y which is assigned to x by f will be called the *image* of the point x under the function f. Frequently, $f(x)$ is also called the *value* of the function f at the point x.

Let A be an arbitrary subset of the domain X of the given function f. By the *image* of A under f, we mean the subset $f(A)$ of the range Y of f which consists of the points $f(x)$ for all $x \in A$; in symbols, we have

$$f(A) = \{f(x) \in Y \mid x \in A\}.$$

In particular, the image $f(X)$ of the whole domain X will be simply called the *image* of the function f and denoted by the symbol Im (f).

PROPOSITION 5.1. *If A and B are any two subsets of the domain X of a function $f:X \rightarrow Y$, then we have*

(a) $$f(A \cup B) = f(A) \cup f(B)$$
(b) $$f(A \cap B) \subset f(A) \cap f(B).$$

Proof. To prove (a), let y denote an arbitrary element in $f(A \cup B)$. By definition, there exists an $x \in A \cup B$ with $f(x) = y$. Since x is in $A \cup B$, we must have $x \in A$ or $x \in B$. Since $y = f(x)$, this implies $y \in f(A)$ or $y \in f(B)$. Hence we have $y \in f(A) \cup f(B)$. Since y is any element of $f(A \cup B)$, we have proved the inclusion

(i) $$f(A \cup B) \subset f(A) \cup f(B).$$

On the other hand, it is obvious that $f(A) \subset f(A \cup B)$ and $f(B) \subset f(A \cup B)$. This implies the inclusion

(ii) $$f(A \cup B) \supset f(A) \cup f(B).$$

Combining the inclusions (i) and (ii), we obtain the equality (a).

To prove (b), let y denote an arbitrary point in $f(A \cap B)$. By definition, there exists a point $x \in A \cap B$ with $y = f(x)$. Because of $x \in A \cap B$, we have $x \in A$ and $x \in B$. Since $y = f(x)$, this implies $y \in f(A)$ and $y \in f(B)$. Hence we obtain $y \in f(A) \cap f(B)$. Since y is any point in $f(A \cap B)$, we have proved the inclusion (b).||

The two sides of the inclusion (b) are not always equal. For example, let

$$X = \{1, 2\}, \, A = \{1\}, \, B = \{2\}, \, Y = \{y\}$$

and let $f: X \to Y$ denote the only possible function. In this case, we have

$$f(A \cap B) = f(\square) = \square, f(A) \cap f(B) = Y.$$

In case $f(X) = Y$, we shall say that $f: X \to Y$ is a function from X *onto* Y; in this case, the function f is also said to be *surjective*. Hence, a necessary and sufficient condition for a function $f: X \to Y$ to be surjective is that, for every point $y \in Y$, there exists at least one point $x \in X$ with $f(x) = y$. The function $f: N \to Z_p$ in Example (2) is surjective while the function $x^2: R \to R$ in Example (3) is not surjective.

Let B denote an arbitrarily given subset of the range Y of the given function $f: X \to Y$. By the *inverse image* of B under f, we mean the subset $f^{-1}(B)$ of the domain X of f which consists of all points $x \in X$ such that $f(x) \in B$; in symbols, we have

$$f^{-1}(B) = \{x \in X \mid f(x) \in B\}.$$

In particular, we have $f^{-1}(Y) = X$. On the other hand, if B is a singleton with $B = \{y\}$, then $f^{-1}(B)$ is said to be the *inverse image* of the point y under the function f and is denoted by $f^{-1}(y)$. Therefore, an arbitrarily given point $y \in Y$ is in the image $f(X)$ iff $f^{-1}(y)$ is nonempty.

In Example (1), the inverse image $f^{-1}(F)$ consists of all students in this class who failed to pass the midsemester test. In Example (2), the inverse image $f^{-1}(0)$ consists of all natural numbers which are multiples of p. In Example (3), the inverse image of a given real number y under the function x^2 is empty if $y < 0$, is the singleton $\{0\}$ if $y = 0$, and consists of the two square roots $\pm \sqrt{y}$ of y if $y > 0$.

PROPOSITION 5.2. *If A and B are any two subsets of the range Y of a function $f: X \to Y$, then we have*

(a) $$f^{-1}(A \cup B) = f^{-1}(A) \cup f^{-1}(B)$$
(b) $$f^{-1}(A \cap B) = f^{-1}(A) \cap f^{-1}(B)$$
(c) $$f^{-1}(A \backslash B) = f^{-1}(A) \backslash f^{-1}(B).$$

Proof. To establish (a), let x be any point in $f^{-1}(A \cup B)$. Then the image $y = f(x)$ of x must be in $A \cup B$ and hence $y \in A$ or $y \in B$. If $y \in A$, we have $x \in f^{-1}(A)$. Similarly, if $y \in B$, we have $x \in f^{-1}(B)$. Therefore, we obtain $x \in f^{-1}(A) \cup f^{-1}(B)$. Since x is any point in $f^{-1}(A \cup B)$, we have proved the following inclusion

(a1) $$f^{-1}(A \cup B) \subset f^{-1}(A) \cup f^{-1}(B).$$

On the other hand, it is obvious that $f^{-1}(A) \subset f^{-1}(A \cup B)$ and $f^{-1}(B) \subset f^{-1}(A \cup B)$. This implies the following inclusion

(a2) $$f^{-1}(A \cup B) \supset f^{-1}(A) \cup f^{-1}(B).$$

Combining inclusions (a1) and (a2), we obtain the equality (a).

To establish (b), let x be any point in $f^{-1}(A \cap B)$. Then the image $y = f(x)$ of x must be in $A \cap B$. Hence we have $y \in A$ and $y \in B$. Since $y = f(x)$, this implies $x \in f^{-1}(A)$ and $x \in f^{-1}(B)$. Consequently, we have $x \in f^{-1}(A) \cap f^{-1}(B)$. Since x is any point in $f^{-1}(A \cap B)$, we have proved the following inclusion

(b1) $$f^{-1}(A \cap B) \subset f^{-1}(A) \cap f^{-1}(B).$$

On the other hand, let x denote any point in $f^{-1}(A) \cap f^{-1}(B)$. Then we have $x \in f^{-1}(A)$ and $x \in f^{-1}(B)$. This implies that the image $y = f(x)$ of x must be both in A and in B. Consequently, we have $y \in A \cap B$. Hence $x \in f^{-1}(A \cap B)$. Since x is any point in $f^{-1}(A) \cap f^{-1}(B)$, we have proved the following inclusion

(b2) $$f^{-1}(A \cap B) \supset f^{-1}(A) \cap f^{-1}(B).$$

Combining the inclusions (b1) and (b2), we obtain the equality (b).

To establish (c), let x denote any point in $f^{-1}(A \backslash B)$. Then the image $y = f(x)$ of x must be in $A \backslash B$. Hence we have $y \in A$ and $y \notin B$. Since $y = f(x)$, this implies $x \in f^{-1}(A)$ and $x \notin f^{-1}(B)$. Consequently, we have $x \in f^{-1}(A) \backslash f^{-1}(B)$. Since x is any point in $f^{-1}(A \backslash B)$, we have proved the following inclusion

(c1) $$f^{-1}(A \backslash B) \subset f^{-1}(A) \backslash f^{-1}(B).$$

On the other hand, let x denote any point in $f^{-1}(A) \backslash f^{-1}(B)$. Then we have $x \in f^{-1}(A)$ and $x \notin f^{-1}(B)$. Let $y = f(x)$. It follows that $y \in A$ and $y \notin B$. Consequently, we have $y \in A \backslash B$. This implies that $x \in f^{-1}(A \backslash B)$.

Since x is any point in $f^{-1}(A)\setminus f^{-1}(B)$, we have proved the following inclusion:

(c2) $$f^{-1}(A\setminus B) \supset f^{-1}(A)\setminus f^{-1}(B).$$

Combining the inclusions (c1) and (c2), we obtain the equality (c).$\|$

By a comparison of the propositions (5.1) and (5.2), one can readily find that the inverse images of functions behave much better than the images.

Let A and B denote any two disjoint subsets of Y. It follows from the equality (b) in (5.2) that the inverse images $f^{-1}(A)$ and $f^{-1}(B)$ are also disjoint. As a special case, the inverse images of distinct points of Y are disjoint.

A function $f:X \to Y$ is said to be *one-to-one* or *injective* iff the images of distinct points of X are distinct; in other words, f is injective iff, for any two points a and b of X, $a \neq b$ implies $f(a) \neq f(b)$. Furthermore, it is not difficult to see that $f:X \to Y$ is injective iff, for each $y \in Y$, the inverse image $f^{-1}(y)$ is either empty or a singleton.

As an illustrative example of injective functions, let us consider the case where X is a subset of a given set Y. The function $i:X \to Y$, which is defined by $i(x) = x \in Y$ for each $x \in X$, will be called the *inclusion function* of X into Y. Obviously, every inclusion function is injective.

A function $f:X \to Y$ is said to be *bijective* iff it is both surjective and injective. Let $f:X \to Y$ be a bijective function. Then, for each point y of Y, the inverse image $f^{-1}(y)$ of y is always a singleton, that is, a single point in X. The assignment $y \to f^{-1}(y)$ defines a function from Y into X which is called the *inverse function* of f and is denoted by

$$f^{-1}:Y \to X.$$

Obviously, f^{-1} is also a bijective function.

EXAMPLES OF BIJECTIVE FUNCTIONS

(a) *The identity functions.* For any given set X, the inclusion function $i:X \to X$ of X into itself is obviously bijective. This special inclusion function i is called the *identity function* on the set X. In this case, we obviously have

$$i^{-1} = i.$$

(b) *The linear functions.* Let $a \neq 0$ and b denote arbitrarily given real numbers. Consider the function

$$f:R \to R$$

defined by $f(x) = ax + b$ for every real number x. This function is called the *linear function* of real variable x with a and b as coefficients and, customarily, is denoted by the equation

$$y = ax + b.$$

By means of high school algebra, one can easily show that this function f is bijective. To find the inverse function f^{-1} of f, we solve the equation for x and obtain

$$x = a^{-1}y - a^{-1}b.$$

Thus, the inverse function $g = f^{-1}$ of f is another linear function defined by $g(y) = a^{-1}y - a^{-1}b$ for every real number y.

EXERCISES

5A. Let A be an arbitrary subset of the domain X of any given function $f:X \rightarrow Y$. Establish the following inclusions:
 (a) $A \subset f^{-1}[f(A)]$
 (b) $f(X) \backslash f(A) \subset f(X \backslash A)$.

5B. Let B be an arbitrary subset of the range Y of any given function $f:X \rightarrow Y$. Establish the following inclusions:
 (a) $f[f^{-1}(B)] \subset B$
 (b) $f^{-1}(Y \backslash B) = X \backslash f^{-1}(B)$.

5C. Establish the following equality for any function $f:X \rightarrow Y$ with $A \subset X$ and $B \subset Y$:

$$f[A \cap f^{-1}(B)] = f(A) \cap B.$$

5D. Find the inverse functions of the following bijective functions:
 (a) The function $T_a:R \rightarrow R$ of the set R of all real numbers defined by $T_a(x) = x + a$ for every $x \in R$, where a stands for a given real number
 (b) The function $S_a:R \rightarrow R$ of the set R of all real numbers defined by $S_a(x) = ax$ for every $x \in R$, where a stands for a given nonzero real number
 (c) The function $f:(-\pi/2, \pi/2) \rightarrow R$ of the open interval $(-\pi/2, \pi/2)$ of all real numbers x satisfying $-\pi/2 < x < \pi/2$ defined by $f(x) = \tan x$ for every $x \in (-\pi/2, \pi/2)$
 (d) The function $f:R \rightarrow P$ of the set R onto the set P of all positive real numbers defined by $f(x) = e^x$ for every $x \in R$, where $e = 2.71828 \cdots$ stands for the base of the natural logarithm

5E. Let X be a given set. For each subset A of X, define a function $\chi_A : X \to R$ by taking

$$\chi_A(x) = \begin{cases} 1 & \text{(if } x \in A) \\ 0 & \text{(if } x \in X \backslash A). \end{cases}$$

This function χ_A is usually called the *characteristic function* of A in X. Prove the following equalities for the characteristic functions of subsets of the set X at any point x of X:

(a) $\chi_{A \cap B}(x) = \chi_A(x) \chi_B(x)$
(b) $\chi_{A \cup B}(x) = \chi_A(x) + \chi_B(x) - \chi_A(x) \chi_B(x)$
(c) $\chi_{A \backslash B}(x) = \chi_A(x)[1 - \chi_B(x)]$.

6. COMPOSITION OF FUNCTIONS

Any two functions f and g are said to be *composable* iff the range of f is equal to the domain of g; in diagram,

$$X \xrightarrow{\;f\;} Y \xrightarrow{\;g\;} Z.$$

In this case, we may define a function

$$h : X \to Z$$

by assigning to every point $x \in X$ the point

$$h(x) = g[f(x)]$$

of the set Z. This function h will be called the *composition* of the given functions f and g denoted by

$$h = g \circ f : X \to Z.$$

For example, let $f, g : R \to R$ denote the functions defined by

$$f(x) = 2x + 3$$
$$g(x) = x^2$$

for every $x \in R$. Then the compositions $h = g \circ f$ and $k = f \circ g$ are both defined; in fact, they are given by

$$h(x) = g[f(x)] = (2x + 3)^2$$
$$k(x) = f[g(x)] = 2x^2 + 3$$

for every real number x. This example shows that $f \circ g$ and $g \circ f$ are usually different, even if both of them are defined. Hence the composition of functions is, in general, noncommutative.

The *composed functions* such as $g \circ f$ given above are customarily called the *functions of functions* in calculus.

PROPOSITION 6.1. *The composition of functions is associative; precisely, for any three composable functions:*

$$W \xleftarrow{\quad h \quad} Z \xleftarrow{\quad g \quad} Y \xleftarrow{\quad f \quad} X$$

we always have

$$h \circ (g \circ f) = (h \circ g) \circ f.$$

Proof. Here, we have to prove that the following two composed functions

$$\phi = h \circ (g \circ f) \qquad \psi = (h \circ g) \circ f$$

from X into W are equal; i.e., for every $x \in X$, we should have $\phi(x) = \psi(x)$.

For this purpose, let x denote an arbitrarily given element in the set X. By the definition of composition, we have

$$\phi(x) = h[(g \circ f)(x)] = h\{g[f(x)]\}$$
$$\psi(x) = (h \circ g)[f(x)] = h\{g[f(x)]\}.$$

Since the extreme right members of these two equalities are the same, we have $\phi(x) = \psi(x)$. Because x is any element of X, this implies $\phi = \psi$. ‖

For the images and the inverse images under a composed function, we have the following proposition.

PROPOSITION 6.2. *If $h = g \circ f$ denotes the composition of two arbitrarily given functions $f: X \to Y$ and $g: Y \to Z$, then the following two statements hold:*

(a) $h(A) = g[f(A)]$ *for every $A \subset X$*
(b) $h^{-1}(C) = f^{-1}[g^{-1}(C)]$ *for every $C \subset Z$.*

Proof. Statement (a) is obvious, since by definition $h(x) = g[f(x)]$ holds for every $x \in X$.

To establish (b), let x denote an arbitrary element in $h^{-1}(C)$. Let $y = f(x)$ and $z = h(x)$. Then the element

$$z = h(x) = g[f(x)] = g(y)$$

must be in the set C. This implies $y \in g^{-1}(C)$. Since $f(x) = y$, it follows that $x \in f^{-1}[g^{-1}(C)]$. Since x is any element in $h^{-1}(C)$, we have proved the following inclusion

(i) $$h^{-1}(C) \subset f^{-1}[g^{-1}(C)].$$

On the other hand, let x denote an arbitrary element in $f^{-1}[g^{-1}(C)]$. Then it follows that $f(x) \in g^{-1}(C)$ and hence $h(x) = g[f(x)] \in C$. This implies $x \in h^{-1}(C)$. Since x is any element in $f^{-1}[g^{-1}(C)]$, we have proved the following inclusion:

(ii) $$h^{-1}(C) \supset f^{-1}[g^{-1}(C)].$$

Combining the inclusions (i) and (ii), we obtain (b).$\|$

As immediate consequences of (6.2), the composition of any two surjective functions is a surjective function and the composition of any two injective functions is an injective function. In particular, the composition of any two bijective functions is a bijective function.

For a partial converse of these facts, we have the following proposition.

PROPOSITION 6.3. *Let $h = g \circ f$ denote the composition of the functions $f:X \to Y$ and $g:Y \to Z$. Then the following two statements are true:*

(a) *If h is surjective, then so is g.*
(b) *If h is injective, then so is f.*

Proof. To establish (a), let us assume that h is surjective. By definition, we have $h(X) = Z$. From (a) of (6.2), it follows that

$$Z = h(X) = g[f(X)] \subset g(Y) \subset Z.$$

This implies that $g(Y) = Z$ and, therefore, g is surjective. Thus we have proved (a).

To establish (b), let us assume that h is injective. Consider any two points a and b of X such that $f(a) = f(b)$. It follows that

$$h(a) = g[f(a)] = g[f(b)] = h(b).$$

Since h is injective, this implies $a = b$. Therefore, f is injective.$\|$

COROLLARY 6.4. *Let $f:X \to Y$ and $g:Y \to X$ denote given functions. If the compositions $g \circ f$ and $f \circ g$ are the identity functions on X and Y, respectively, then both f and g are bijective and each is the inverse function of the other.*

Proof. Since the composition $g \circ f$ is bijective, it follows from (6.3) that f is injective and g is surjective. On the other hand, since $f \circ g$ is bijective, it follows that f is surjective and g is injective. Therefore, both f and g are bijective.

To prove that g is the inverse function of f, let y denote any point in Y. Since f is bijective, there exists a unique point $x \in X$ with $f(x) = y$. Hence we have $f^{-1}(y) = x$. Since $g \circ f$ is the identity function on X, we have

$$g(y) = g[f(x)] = (g \circ f)(x) = x = f^{-1}(y).$$

Since y is any point in Y, this proves $g = f^{-1}$.
Similarly, one can prove $f = g^{-1}$.$\|$

COROLLARY 6.5.   *For an arbitrarily given bijective function $f:X \to Y$, f is the inverse function of $f^{-1}:Y \to X$.*

Proof.   By the definition of the inverse function f^{-1} of the bijective function, it is evident that the compositions $f^{-1} \circ f$ and $f \circ f^{-1}$ are the identity functions on X and Y, respectively. Hence (6.4) implies (6.5).‖

Now let us consider a given function $f:X \to Y$ and an arbitrary subset A of X. We may define a function $g:A \to Y$ by setting

$$g(x) = f(x)$$

for every element x of A. This new function g is called the *restriction* of the given function f to the subset A and is denoted by the symbol

$$g = f \mid A.$$

Whenever $g = f \mid A$, the function f is called an *extension* of the function g over the set X. In this case, we have a triangle

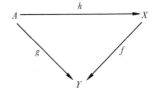

FIGURE 5

of sets and functions, where h denotes the inclusion function. Here, the relation $g = f \mid A$ is equivalent to the condition $g = f \circ h$. Such a triangle is said to be *commutative* iff $g = f \circ h$ holds.

Although there is only one restriction of a given function $f:X \to Y$ to a given subset A of X, the extensions of a given function $g:A \to Y$ over a larger set X which contains A are, in general, very many. For example, let b denote any point in Y; then the function $f_b:X \to Y$ defined by

$$f_b(x) = \begin{cases} g(x), & (\text{if } x \in A) \\ b, & (\text{if } x \in X \setminus A) \end{cases}$$

is an extension of g over the set X.

EXERCISES

6A. Find the compositions $f \circ g$ and $g \circ f$ of the functions f, $g:R \to R$ defined for each real number $x \in R$ as follows:

    (a) $f(x) = x + 2$ and $g(x) = 3x$

    (b) $f(x) = x^2 + x + 1$ and $g(x) = x + 1$

(c) $f(x) = e^x$ and $g(x) = \sin x$

(d) $f(x) = x^2$ and $g(x) = \cos x$.

6B. Consider the functions $f:R \to R\backslash\{0\}$ and $g:R\backslash\{0\} \to P$ defined by $f(x) = e^x$ and $g(y) = y^2$ for every $x \in R$ and every $y \in R\backslash\{0\}$, where R stands for the set of all real numbers and P denotes the set of all positive real numbers. Verify that the composition $g \circ f:R \to P$ is a bijective function while f is not surjective nor g injective.

6C. Consider an arbitrarily given function $f:X \to Y$ and denote the image $f(X)$ by B. Let $i:B \to Y$ denote the inclusion function and define a function $j:X \to B$ by taking $j(x) = f(x) \in B$ for every $x \in X$. Show that i is injective, that j is surjective, and that $i \circ j = f$. Hence, every function can be decomposed into the composition of a surjective function and an injective function.

7. CARTESIAN PRODUCTS OF SETS

Consider the Euclidean plane R^2 of analytic geometry. The points of R^2 are the pairs of real numbers (x, y). Two points (x_1, y_1) and (x_2, y_2) of R^2 are equal iff $x_1 = x_2$ and $y_1 = y_2$. Thus, $(1, 3)$ is not equal to $(3, 1)$. Because of this, the points (x, y) of R^2 are frequently called *ordered pairs* of real numbers. This set R^2 is an example of the Cartesian product of two given sets which is a fundamental concept used in many constructions given in this text.

Let X and Y denote any two given sets. By the *Cartesian product* of X and Y, we mean the set $X \times Y$ of all pairs (x, y) with $x \in X$ and $y \in Y$; in symbols, we have

$$X \times Y = \{(x, y) \mid x \in X \quad \text{and} \quad y \in Y\}.$$

Hence, the Euclidean plane R^2 is the Cartesian product $R \times R$ of the set R of all real numbers with itself.

Now let M denote the set which consists of two members, namely, the integers 1 and 2. Then the Cartesian product $X \times Y$ can be considered as the set F of all functions

$$f:M \to X \cup Y$$

such that $f(1) \in X$ and $f(2) \in Y$. To see this, let us define a function

$$j:F \to X \times Y$$

by taking $j(f) = [f(1), f(2)]$ for every $f \in F$. It is very easy to verify that j is bijective. Hence we can generalize the important notion of Cartesian products as follows.

Let us consider an arbitrarily given family Φ of sets. The members of Φ are given sets. In order to distinguish each of these sets from the others, we usually label these sets by means of subscripts called *indices*. Let M denote the set of all indices which we have used to label the sets in Φ, and let X_μ stand for the set in Φ which is labeled by the index $\mu \in M$. Thus, we have

$$\Phi = \{X_\mu \mid \mu \in M\}.$$

Such a family Φ of sets is called an *indexed family* of sets. The set M will be referred to as the *set of indices* of the family Φ.

Let $\Phi = \{X_\mu \mid \mu \in M\}$ be an arbitrarily given indexed family of sets. We define the *union*

$$U = \bigcup_{\mu \in M} X_\mu$$

of this family by requiring $x \in U$ iff there exists a $\mu \in M$ such that $x \in X_\mu$. Then the *Cartesian product*

$$P = \Pi_{\mu \in M} X_\mu$$

of this family Φ is defined to be the set of all functions $f : M \to U$ such that $(\mu) \in X_\mu$ for every index $\mu \in M$.

In case M consists of two members, namely, the integers 1 and 2, with $X_1 = X$ and $X_2 = Y$, then we have

$$U = X \cup Y \qquad P = X \times Y.$$

As another example, if M consists of three members, say, the integers 1, 2, 3, and if $X_\mu = R$ for every $\mu = 1, 2, 3$, then the Cartesian product

$$P = R \times R \times R = R^3$$

is the *three-dimensional Euclidean space* of solid analytic geometry. Each point of R^3 is actually an ordered triple (x_1, x_2, x_3) of real numbers.

Slightly more generally, if M consists of the first n positive integers, then a point f in P is essentially an ordered n-tuple $(x_1, \ldots, x_n)$ with $x_i = f(i)$ for every integer $i = 1, \ldots, n$. In this finite case, the Cartesian product of the family Φ is usually denoted by

$$P = X_1 \times \cdots \times X_n.$$

As another special case, if every set X_μ in the family Φ is equal to a given set X, then the Cartesian product P of the family Φ is called the *Mth Cartesian power* of the given set X and will be denoted by

$$P = X^M.$$

Therefore, X^M consists of all functions from M into X. In particular, if

M is the set of the first n positive integers, then P will be referred to as the *nth Cartesian power* of the given set X and will be denoted by

$$P = X^n.$$

Hence, X^n is the set of all ordered n-tuples $(x_1, \ldots, x_n)$ with $x_i \in X$ for each $i = 1, \ldots, n$.

In case $X = R$, the nth Cartesian power R^n of the set R of all real numbers is the *n-dimensional Euclidean space* of higher analytic geometry. The points of R^n are the ordered n-tuples $(x_1, \ldots, x_n)$ of real numbers.

Now let us return to our general case. For each index $\mu \in M$, consider the function

$$p_\mu : P \to X_\mu$$

which is defined by $p_\mu(f) = f(\mu)$ for every $f \in P$. This function p_μ will be called the *natural projection* of the Cartesian product P upon its μth coordinate set X_μ.

For our important special case $P = X \times Y$, we will let

$$p : X \times Y \to X \qquad q : X \times Y \to Y$$

denote the natural projections. These are defined by

$$p(x, y) = x \qquad q(x, y) = y$$

for every point (x, y) of the Cartesian product $X \times Y$.

PROPOSITION 7.1.   *If the sets X and Y are both nonempty, then the natural projections p and q are surjective.*

Proof.   To prove that p is surjective, let x denote an arbitrary element in X. Since Y is nonempty, there is at least one element $y \in Y$. Then (x, y) is by definition a point of the Cartesian product $X \times Y$. Since $p(x, y) = x$ and x is any element of X, we have proved that p is surjective. Similarly, one can prove that q is also surjective.$\|$

Obviously one can generalize (7.1) to Cartesian product of more sets.

By means of the Cartesian product $X \times Y$, we can define the *graph* of any given function $f : X \to Y$ to be the subset $G = \mathrm{Gr}(f)$ of $X \times Y$ defined by

$$G = \mathrm{Gr}(f) = \{(x, y) \in X \times Y \mid f(x) = y\}.$$

For example, the graph of the function $x^2 : R \to R$ is the parabola $y = x^2$ in the Euclidean plane R^2.

The graph of the identity function on a set X is called the *diagonal* of the *Cartesian square* $X^2 = X \times X$ denoted by $\triangle(X^2)$. In symbols, the diagonal $\triangle(X^2)$ of X^2 is defined by

$$\triangle(X^2) = \{(x, y) \in X^2 \mid y = x\}.$$

In particular, if $X = R$, then the diagonal of the Euclidean plane R^2 is the line defined by the linear equation $y = x$.

The graph of a function has the following important property.

PROPOSITION 7.2. *For any given function $f:X \to Y$, the restriction $j = p \mid G$ of the natural projection $p:X \times Y \to X$ to the graph $G = \mathrm{Gr}(f)$ of f is a bijective function from G onto X.*

Proof. To prove that j is surjective, let x denote any point in X and let $y = f(x) \in Y$. Then we have $(x, y) \in G$ by definition. Since $j = p \mid G$, we get

$$j(x, y) = p(x, y) = x.$$

Since x is any point in X, we have proved that j is surjective.

To prove that j is injective, let (x_1, y_1) and (x_2, y_2) denote any two points of G such that $j(x_1, y_1) = j(x_2, y_2)$. Then we have

$$x_1 = j(x_1, y_1) = j(x_2, y_2) = x_2.$$

By definition of the graph G of f, we get

$$y_1 = f(x_1) = f(x_2) = y_2.$$

Hence $(x_1, y_1) = (x_2, y_2)$. This implies that j is also injective.$\|$

Obviously, the inverse function of the bijective function $j:G \to X$ in (7.2) is the bijective function

$$f^*:X \to G$$

defined by $f^*(x) = (x, f(x)) \in G$ for every point x in X. This bijective function f^* is said to be induced by the given function $f:X \to Y$.

The graphs of functions are actually characterized by the property in (7.2). Precisely, we have the following proposition.

PROPOSITION 7.3. *Let G be any given subset of the Cartesian product $X \times Y$ of two given sets X and Y. If the restriction $j = p \mid G$ of the natural projection $p:X \times Y \to X$ is a bijective function from G onto X, then there exists a unique function $f:X \to Y$ with $\mathrm{Gr}(f) = G$.*

Proof. To construct a function $f:X \to Y$ with $\mathrm{Gr}(f) = G$, let x denote an arbitrary point of X. Since j is a bijective function from G onto X, there exists a unique point $(x, y) \in G$ such that

$$j(x, y) = p(x, y) = x.$$

We assign to $x \in X$ the point $f(x) = y \in Y$. Since x is any point in X, this defines a function $f:X \to Y$. Since $(x, f(x))$ is the only point of G with x its first coordinate, it follows that

$$\begin{aligned} G &= \{[x, f(x)] \in X \times Y \mid x \in X\} \\ &= \{(x, y) \in X \times Y \mid y = f(x)\} = \mathrm{Gr}(f). \end{aligned}$$

To prove the uniqueness of the function, let us assume that $f, g : X \to Y$ are any two functions with

$$\mathrm{Gr}(f) = G = \mathrm{Gr}(g).$$

We have to prove $f = g$. For this purpose, let x denote any point in X. By the definition of graphs, both the points $[x, f(x)]$ and $[x, g(x)]$ are in G. Since

$$j[x, f(x)] = x = j[x, g(x)]$$

and j is bijective, it follows that

$$[x, f(x)] = [x, g(x)]$$

and hence we have $f(x) = g(x)$. Since x is any point in X, we have $f = g$. This proves the uniqueness of f. $\|$

According to (7.2) and (7.3), any function $f : X \to Y$ determines its graph $\mathrm{Gr}(f)$ and is completely determined by $\mathrm{Gr}(f)$. Besides, there is a bijective correspondence between the functions $f : X \to Y$ and the subsets G of $X \times Y$ such that $p \mid G$ is bijective. This gives rise to the so-called "sets of ordered pairs" definition of functions.

EXERCISES

7A. Let X and Y be arbitrarily given sets. Prove that the assignment $(x, y) \to (y, x)$ for each $x \in X$ and each $y \in Y$ defines a bijective function

$$f : X \times Y \to Y \times X.$$

Thus the Cartesian products $X \times Y$ and $Y \times X$ are essentially the same.

7B. Let $A \subset X$ and $B \subset Y$ denote any subsets of given sets X and Y. Prove the following relations:
   (a) $A \times B \subset X \times Y$
   (b) $(X \times Y) \backslash (A \times B) = [(X \backslash A) \times Y] \cup [X \times (Y \backslash B)]$.

7C. Let $A \subset X$, $B \subset Y$, $C \subset X$, and $D \subset Y$ denote subsets of given sets X and Y. Prove the following relations:
   (a) $(A \times B) \cap (C \times D) = (A \cap C) \times (B \cap D)$
   (b) $(A \times B) \cup (C \times D) \subset (A \cup C) \times (B \cup D)$.
   Give an example which shows that $(A \cup C) \times (B \cup D)$ is not necessarily contained in $(A \times B) \cup (C \times D)$.

7D. Draw the graphs of the functions $f:R \to R$ defined for each real number $x \in R$ as follows:

(a) $f(x) = 2x - 3$
(b) $f(x) = x^2$
(c) $f(x) = x^3$
(d) $f(x) = e^x$
(e) $f(x) = \sin x$.

7E. Let $f:X \to U$ and $g:Y \to V$ be any two given functions. Show that the assignment $(x, y) \to [f(x), g(y)]$ for each $x \in X$ and each $y \in Y$ defines a function

$$h:X \times Y \to U \times V.$$

This function h is called the *Cartesian product* of the given functions f and g, and will be denoted by $f \times g$. Prove the following statements:

(a) If f and g are injective, so is $f \times g$.
(b) If f and g are surjective, so is $f \times g$.

8. RELATIONS IN A SET

Let us consider the set R of all real numbers and the relation $<$ in the usual sense. Then, for any two real numbers $x, y \in R$, we have the fact that $x < y$ holds iff the point (x, y) of the Euclidean plane R^2 is above the diagonal $\triangle$ of R^2. Therefore, if we denote by U the set of all points of R^2 lying above its diagonal $\triangle$, then the relation $<$ can be defined by the set $U \subset R^2$, i.e.

$$x < y \Leftrightarrow (x, y) \in U.$$

This suggests the following notion of a relation in an arbitrarily given set. By a *relation* in a given set X, we mean a subset $\Re$ of the Cartesian square $X^2 = X \times X$ of the given set X. For example, let X denote the set of all living people on the earth. Then the marriage relation in X means the subset $\mathfrak{M}$ of the Cartesian square X^2 consisting of the couples $(a, b) \in X^2$ such that a is married to b.

Consider an arbitrarily given relation $\Re$ in a set X and let a, b denote any two members of X. If the point (a, b) of the Cartesian square X^2 is in its subset $\Re$, then we shall say that a is *related to* b with respect to the given relation $\Re$; in symbols, we denote

$$a \,\Re\, b.$$

In the example of the marriage relation $\mathfrak{M}$ in the set X of all living people on the earth, $a \,\mathfrak{M}\, b$ means that a is married to b.

If $a \, \mathfrak{R} \, a$ holds for every member a of the set X, then we say that the given relation $\mathfrak{R}$ in X is *reflexive*. For example, the relation $\leqslant$ in the set R of all real numbers is reflexive, while the relation $<$ in the same set R is not reflexive. Also, the marriage relation $\mathfrak{M}$ in the set X of all living people on the earth is not reflexive.

If $a \, \mathfrak{R} \, b$ implies $b \, \mathfrak{R} \, a$ for any two members a and b of the given set X, then we say that the relation $\mathfrak{R}$ is *symmetric*. For example, the marriage relation $\mathfrak{M}$ in the set X of all living people on the earth is symmetric, while neither of the relations $\leqslant$ and $<$ in the set R of all real numbers is symmetric.

If $a \, \mathfrak{R} \, b$ and $b \, \mathfrak{R} \, c$ imply $a \, \mathfrak{R} \, c$ for arbitrary members a, b, c of the given set X, then we say that the relation $\mathfrak{R}$ is *transitive*. For example, both of the relations $\leqslant$ and $<$ in the set R of all real numbers are transitive, while the marriage relation $\mathfrak{M}$ in the set X of all living people on the earth is not transitive.

A relation $\mathfrak{R}$ in a set X will be called an *equivalence relation* in X iff it is reflexive, symmetric, and transitive. Equivalence relations are usually denoted by the symbol $\sim$.

EXAMPLES OF EQUIVALENCE RELATIONS

(1) Let X denote the set of all students in this class. Define a relation $\sim$ in X as follows: For any two members a and b of X, we define $a \sim b$ iff a and b are of the same age. One can easily see that this relation $\sim$ in X is reflexive, symmetric, and transitive. Therefore, $\sim$ is an equivalence relation in X.

(2) Let p denote a given positive integer. Define a relation $\sim$ in the set $\mathcal{Z}$ of all integers as follows: For any two integers a and b in $\mathcal{Z}$, we define $a \sim b$ iff $b - a$ is divisible by p. One can easily verify that this relation $\sim$ in $\mathcal{Z}$ is reflexive, symmetric, and transitive. Therefore, $\sim$ is an equivalence relation in $\mathcal{Z}$, usually called the *congruence mod p*. If $a \sim b$ holds in this relation, then we say that a and b are *congruent mod p*; in symbols,

$$a \equiv b \bmod p.$$

(3) Let $f : X \to Y$ denote a given function. Define a relation $\sim$ in the set X as follows: For any two elements a and b in X, we define $a \sim b$ iff $f(a) = f(b)$ holds. One can easily verify that this relation $\sim$ in X is reflexive, symmetric, and transitive. Therefore, $\sim$ is an equivalence relation in X.

Now let us consider an arbitrarily given equivalence relation $\sim$ in a set X. For any two members a and b of the set X, we say that a is *equivalent* to b iff $a \sim b$ holds. For every member a of the set X, let $C(a)$ denote the subset of X whose members are the elements of X which are equivalent to a; in symbols, we have

$$C(a) = \{x \in X \mid x \sim a\}.$$

Since $\sim$ is reflexive, the following lemma is obvious.

LEMMA 8.1. *For every member a of the set X, we have $a \in C(a)$.*

Next, let us establish the following lemma.

LEMMA 8.2. *For any two members a and b of the set X, we must have either $C(a) \cap C(b) = \square$ or $C(a) = C(b)$.*

Proof. Assume that $C(a) \cap C(b) \neq \square$ holds. It suffices to prove $C(a) = C(b)$. For this purpose, let c denote a common member of $C(a)$ and $C(b)$.

To prove $C(a) \subset C(b)$, let x denote any member of the set $C(a)$. Then it follows from the definition of $C(a)$ that $x \sim a$ holds. Since c is a common member of $C(a)$ and $C(b)$, we must have $c \sim a$ and $c \sim b$. Since $\sim$ is symmetric, we have

$$x \sim a \sim c \sim b.$$

Because of the transitivity of $\sim$, this implies $x \sim b$ and hence $x \in C(b)$. Since x is any member of $C(a)$, we have proved the inclusion $C(a) \subset C(b)$.

Similarly, we can also prove the inclusion $C(b) \subset C(a)$. Hence we obtain the equality $C(a) = C(b)$.‖

According to the lemmas (8.1) and (8.2), the distinct members of the family $\{C(a) \mid a \in X\}$ of subsets of X are nonempty and mutually disjoint. These subsets of X are called the *equivalence classes* of $\sim$ in the set X, and the subset $C(a)$ of X is said to be the *equivalence class* of the element $a \in X$ with respect to the given equivalence relation $\sim$.

A family $\mathcal{P}$ of mutually disjoint nonempty subsets of a given set X is called a *partition* of the set X iff the union of all members of $\mathcal{P}$ is the whole set X. Since $a \in C(a)$ holds for every $a \in X$, it follows immediately that the family Q of all distinct equivalent classes of $\sim$ in the given set X is a partition of X. This set Q will be called the *quotient set* of the given set X over the equivalent relation $\sim$ and will be denoted by

$$Q = X/\sim.$$

Now let us go back to the examples of equivalence relations given above.

In (1), the equivalence classes are the different age groups of the students in this class, and the quotient set Q consists of these age groups as members.

In (**2**), the equivalence classes are usually called the *congruence mod p* classes of the integers, and the quotient set

$$Z_p = Z/\sim$$

which consists of the p congruence mod p classes $C(0)$, $C(1)$, . . . , $C(p-1)$ is called the *set of integers mod p*. The p members of Z_p will also be referred to as the *integers mod p*.

In (**3**), the equivalence classes are the nonempty inverse images $f^{-1}(y)$ for all $y \, \epsilon \, f(X) \subset Y$. This assignment $y \rightarrow f^{-1}(y)$ defines a bijective function from the image $f(X)$ of f onto the quotient set $Q = X/\sim$.

The function $p:X \rightarrow Q$ defined by taking

$$p(a) = C(a) \, \epsilon \, Q$$

for every member $a \, \epsilon \, X$ will be called the *natural projection* of the set X onto its quotient set Q. The following proposition is obvious.

PROJECTION 8.3. *The natural projection $p:X \rightarrow Q$ is always surjective.*

By a *partial order* in any given set X, we mean a transitive relation in the set X.

For an example, consider the set N of all natural numbers and define a relation $<$ by setting $a < b$ iff $b - a$ belongs to N. One can easily verify the transitivity of $<$ and hence $<$ is a partial order in N. This partial order $<$ is called the *usual order* in N.

For another example, consider the set $X = 2^M$ of all subsets of a given set M. The inclusion $\subset$ obviously defines a partial order in the set X.

A partial order $<$ in a given set X will be called a *linear order* in X iff the following two conditions are satisfied:

(**L1**) For any two members a and b of the set X, $a < b$ and $b < a$ imply $a = b$.

(**L2**) For any two distinct members a and b of the set X, we have $a < b$ or $b < a$.

For example, the usual order $<$ in the set N of all natural numbers is a linear order, while the partial order $\subset$ defined in the set $X = 2^M$ is not a linear order if M consists of more than one point.

Finally, let X denote a set together with a linear order $<$ in X. Then X is said to be *well-ordered* iff every nonempty subset S of the set X has a *least member*, i.e., a member a of S such that $a < b$ holds for each member b of S other than a. For example, the set N of all natural numbers is well-ordered with respect to its usual order.

EXERCISES

8A. Let X denote the set of all living Americans. Investigate the following relations in X with regard to reflexivity, symmetry, and transitivity. Determine which of these are equivalence relations in X and which of these are partial orders in X:
   (a) Is married to
   (b) Is younger than
   (c) Is of the same age as
   (d) Is of the same sex as
   (e) Is a friend of
   (f) Is a parent of
   (g) Is a descendant of.

8B. Let X and Y be arbitrary sets with given equivalence relations in X and Y, both denoted by the same symbol $\sim$. A function $f:X \to Y$ is said to *preserve* the equivalence relation $\sim$ iff, for any two members a and b of X, $a \sim b$ implies $f(a) \sim f(b)$. Assume that $f:X \to Y$ preserves $\sim$. Prove that the image $f(C)$ of any equivalence class C of X is contained in a unique equivalence class D of Y. Hence the assignment $C \to D$ defines a function

$$f^*:X/\sim \;\to\; Y/\sim,$$

called the *induced function* of f on the quotient sets.

8C. Let X and Y be arbitrary sets with given partial orders in X and Y, both denoted by the same symbol $<$. A function $f:X \to Y$ is said to *preserve* the partial order $<$ (or *increasing*) iff, for any two members a and b of X, $a < b$ implies $f(a) < f(b)$. A function $f:X \to Y$ is said to *reverse* the partial order $<$ (or to *be decreasing*) iff, for any two members a and b of X, $a < b$ implies $f(b) < f(a)$. Consider the following functions $f:R \to R$ of the set R of all real numbers. Determine those which preserve the usual partial order $<$ in R and those which reverse it:
   (a) $f(x) = 3x - 7$ for each $x \in R$
   (b) $f(x) = 1 - 2x$ for each $x \in R$
   (c) $f(x) = x^2$ for each $x \in R$
   (d) $f(x) = x^3$ for each $x \in R$
   (e) $f(x) = e^x$ for each $x \in R$
   (f) $f(x) = e^{-x}$ for each $x \in R$
   (g) $f(x) = -e^{-x}$ for each $x \in R$.

9. CARDINALITY OF A SET

In the first meeting of a class, the professor wanted to make sure that there were enough seats for the students. With this purpose in mind, he requested the students to sit down. If there were no student standing, he was sure that the seats were enough for the class. This sitting-down operation established an injective function

$$f:X \to Y$$

from the set X of all students in the class into the set Y of all seats in the classroom.

Next, he counted the empty seats if there were any so that he should know how many more students he could enroll in the class. If there were no empty seats, then the function $f:X \to Y$ established by the sitting-down operation is bijective. In this case, the (cardinal) number of the set X is equal to that of the set Y. Mathematically, we prefer to say that the sets X and Y are *equipotent* or have *the same cardinality*.

The precise definition of cardinality is as follows: Two sets X and Y are said to *be equipotent* or to *have the same cardinality*, in symbols

$$X \simeq Y,$$

iff there exists a bijective function $f:X \to Y$ from X onto Y.

Since identity functions on sets are bijective, $\simeq$ is a reflexive relation. Since the inverse of any bijective function is bijective, the relation $\simeq$ is symmetric. Finally, since the composition of any two composable bijective functions is also bijective, the relation $\simeq$ is transitive. Hence $\simeq$ is an equivalence relation.

A set X is said to be *infinite* iff there exists a proper subset of X which has the same cardinality as X itself. For example, the set N of all natural numbers is infinite because N is equipotent to its proper subset $2N$ of all even integers as shown by the bijective function

$$f:N \to 2N$$

defined by $f(n) = 2n$ for every $n \in N$.

A set X is said to be *finite* iff it is not infinite.

PROPOSITION 9.1.   *Every subset of a finite set is finite.*

Proof. Let A denote any subset of an arbitrarily given finite set X. To prove the finiteness of A by the indirect method, let us assume A to be infinite. By definition, this implies the existence of a proper subset B of the set A, together with a bijective function

$$f:A \to B$$

from A onto B. Define a function $g:X \to X$ by taking

$$g(x) = \begin{cases} f(x) & \text{(if } x \in A) \\ x & \text{(if } x \in X \backslash A). \end{cases}$$

Then g is obviously injective and the image $\mathrm{Im}(g)$ of g is the subset

$$C = X \backslash (A \backslash B)$$

of X. Since B is a proper subset of A, it follows that $A \backslash B$ is nonempty and hence C is a proper subset of X. Thus we have proved that X has the same cardinality as its proper subset C. This contradicts the hypothesis that X is finite and proves (9.1).‖

PROPOSITION 9.2. *Every set which has the same cardinality as a finite set is finite.*

Proof. Let X denote an arbitrarily given set which has the same cardinality as a finite set F. By definition, there is a bijective function

$$f:X \to F$$

from X onto F. Consider the inverse function

$$g = f^{-1}:F \to X$$

of f which is also bijective.

To prove the finiteness of X by the indirect method, let us assume X to be infinite. Then there exists a bijective function

$$h:X \to A$$

from X onto a proper subset A of X. Making use of the inclusion function

$$i:A \to X$$

we obtain the composed function

$$j = f \circ i \circ h \circ g:F \to F.$$

As a composition of injective functions, j is injective. The image

$$j(F) = f(A)$$

is obviously a proper subset of F. This contradicts the finiteness of F and proves (9.2).‖

COROLLARY 9.3. *Every set which has the same cardinality as an infinite set is infinite.*

Proof. Let X be a set which has the same cardinality as an infinite set G. Then X cannot be finite, for otherwise G would be finite by (9.2).‖

To determine the cardinality of a given finite set X, we usually apply the *counting process*. If the given set X is empty, then we say that the cardinality of the set X is zero. Otherwise, we can pick a member x of X and label it with the least integer 1 in the set N of all natural numbers as a subscript. Thus we obtain a subset

$$X_1 = \{x_1\}$$

of X. If $X \setminus X_1 = \square$; that is, if there is no other member left in X, then X is a singleton and we say that the cardinality of the set X is 1. Otherwise, we can pick a member of $X \setminus X$, and label it with the least integer 2 in the set $N \setminus \{1\}$ as a subscript. Thus we obtain a subset

$$X_2 = \{x_1, x_2\}$$

of X consisting of two distinct members x_1 and x_2 of X. After repeating this process n times, we obtain a subset

$$X_n = \{x_1, x_2, \ldots, x_n\}$$

of X which consists of n distinct members of X. If $X \setminus X_n = \square$, that is, if there is no other member left in X, then $X = X_n$ and we say that the cardinality of the set X is n. In this case, we have a bijective function

$$f : F_n \rightarrow X$$

from the subset

$$F_n = \{1, 2, \ldots, n\}$$

of N onto X defined by $f(i) = x_i$ for every $i \in F_n$. In case $X \setminus X_n \neq \square$, we have to carry the process further. The important fact is that this counting process must terminate sooner or later if the given set X is finite. Precisely, we have the following theorem.

THEOREM 9.4.   *For an arbitrarily given nonempty finite set X, the counting process must terminate and there is a unique positive integer n such that X has the same cardinality as the subset $F_n = \{1, 2, \ldots, n\}$ of the set N of all natural numbers.*

Proof.   Assume that the counting process has been applied on the set X in such a way that it never terminates. Then this process establishes an injective function

$$f : N \rightarrow X$$

of N into X. By (9.3), the image $f(N)$ is infinite. According to (9.1), this implies that X must be infinite. This contradiction proves that the counting process on X must terminate. Hence there exists a positive integer such that X has the same cardinality as the subset F_n of N.

It remains to prove the uniqueness of the positive integer n. For this purpose, let us assume that there are two distinct positive integers m and n with

$$X \simeq F_m \qquad X \simeq F_n.$$

It follows that $F_m \simeq F_n$.

Since m and n are distinct, we may assume without loss of generality that $m < n$. In this case, F_m is a proper subset of F_n. Since $F_m \simeq F_n$, it follows that F_n would be infinite and hence X would be infinite. This contradiction proves (9.4).∥

An infinite set X is said to be *countably infinite* iff X has the same cardinality as the set N of all natural numbers. In other words, X is countably infinite iff there exists a bijective function

$$f: N \to X$$

from N onto X. This bijective function f arranges the members of X in the form of an infinite sequence

$$f(1), f(2), \ldots, f(n), \ldots$$

of distinct terms. Hence a set X is countably infinite iff its members can be arranged in the form of an infinite sequence of distinct terms.

A set X is said to be *countable* iff X is either finite or countably infinite.

LEMMA 9.5. *For an arbitrarily given nonempty set X, the following three statements are equivalent:*

(a) *The set X is countable.*

(b) *There exists a surjective function $f: N \to X$ from the set N of all natural numbers onto the set X.*

(c) *There exists an injective function $g: X \to N$ from the set X into the set N of all natural numbers.*

Proof. To prove the equivalence of the three statements (a), (b), and (c), it suffices to establish the implication

$$(\textbf{a}) \Rightarrow (\textbf{b}), \qquad (\textbf{b}) \Rightarrow (\textbf{c}), \qquad (\textbf{c}) \Rightarrow (\textbf{a}),$$

as shown in the following diagram.

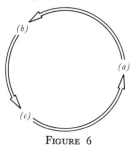

FIGURE 6

The converses of these implications can be obtained as follows: (**b**) $\Rightarrow$ (**c**) and (**c**) $\Rightarrow$ (**a**) imply (**b**) $\Rightarrow$ (**a**); (**c**) $\Rightarrow$ (**a**) and (**a**) $\Rightarrow$ (**b**) imply (**c**) $\Rightarrow$ (**b**); and (**a**) $\Rightarrow$ (**b**) and (**b**) $\Rightarrow$ (**c**) imply (**a**) $\Rightarrow$ (**c**).

(**a**) $\Rightarrow$ (**b**).   Assume X to be countable. Then X is either finite or countably infinite. In case X is finite, it follows from (9.4) that there exists a bijective function $h:F_n \to X$ from the set $F_n = \{1, 2, \ldots, n\}$ onto X for some natural number n. Then h has an extension $f:\mathcal{N} \to X$ given by $f(x) = h(x)$ if $x \in F_n$ and $f(x) = h(n)$ if $x \in \mathcal{N} \backslash F_n$. Since h is surjective, so is f. In case X is countably infinite, it follows from the definition that there exists a bijective function $f:\mathcal{N} \to X$. This proves (**b**).

(**b**) $\Rightarrow$ (**c**).   Let $f:\mathcal{N} \to X$ be a given surjective function. Then, for every member x of X, the inverse image $f^{-1}(x)$ in $\mathcal{N}$ is nonempty and hence we may pick a member $g(x)$ of the set $f^{-1}(x)$. The assignment $x \to g(x)$ defines a function $g:X \to \mathcal{N}$. Since the inverse images of distinct members of X are disjoint subsets of $\mathcal{N}$, it follows that g is injective. This proves (**c**).

(**c**) $\Rightarrow$ (**a**).   Let $g:X \to \mathcal{N}$ be a given injective function. If X is finite, then (**a**) is true. Hereafter we assume that X is infinite. Then the image $g(X)$ is an infinite subset of $\mathcal{N}$ according to (9.3). Define a function $h:\mathcal{N} \to g(X)$ as follows: Let $h(1)$ be the least integer in $g(X)$, and when $h(n)$ has been defined for every $n \in F_m$ for some $m \geqslant 1$, we set $h(m + 1)$ to be the least integer in the set $g(X) \backslash h(F_m)$. It can be easily verified that h is bijective. Making use of the inverse function

$$i = g^{-1}:g(X) \to X$$

we obtain the composed function

$$j = i \circ h:\mathcal{N} \to X.$$

As a composition of bijective functions, j is also bijective. This proves (**a**).$\|$

COROLLARY 9.6.   *Every set which has the same cardinality as a countable set is countable.*

Proof.   Let X denote a given set which has the same cardinality as a countable set C. By definition, there exists a bijective function

$$f:X \to C.$$

Since C is countable, it follows from (**a**) $\Rightarrow$ (**c**) in (9.5) that there exists an injective function

$$g:C \to \mathcal{N}.$$

As a composition of injective functions, the function

$$h = g \circ f : X \to N$$

is also injective. By $(\mathbf{c}) \Rightarrow (\mathbf{a})$ in (9.5), this implies that X is countable.‖

COROLLARY 9.7. *Every subset of a countable set is countable.*

Proof. Let A denote any subset of a countable set X. By $(\mathbf{a}) \Rightarrow (\mathbf{c})$ in (9.5), there exists an injective function

$$g : X \to N.$$

On the other hand, the inclusion function

$$f : A \to X$$

is also injective. As a composition of injective functions,

$$h = g \circ f : A \to N$$

is an injective function. By $(\mathbf{c}) \Rightarrow (\mathbf{a})$ in (9.5), this implies that A is countable.‖

COROLLARY 9.8. *Every quotient set of a countable set is countable.*

Proof. Let Q be any quotient set of a countable set X. By $(\mathbf{a}) \Rightarrow (\mathbf{b})$ in (9.5), there exists a surjective function

$$f : N \to X.$$

On the other hand, the natural projection

$$p : X \to Q$$

is also a surjective function. As a composition of surjective functions,

$$g = p \circ f : N \to Q$$

is a surjective function. By $(\mathbf{b}) \Rightarrow (\mathbf{a})$ in (9.5), this implies that Q is countable.‖

LEMMA 9.9. *The Cartesian square*

$$N^2 = N \times N$$

of the set N of all natural numbers is countable.

Proof. The elements of N^2 are the ordered pairs (i, j) of natural numbers and can be displayed in an array as on the next page.

$$
\begin{array}{lllll}
(1, 1) & (1, 2) & (1, 3) & (1, 4) & \cdots \\
(2, 1) & (2, 2) & (2, 3) & (2, 4) & \cdots \\
(3, 1) & (3, 2) & (3, 3) & (3, 4) & \cdots \\
(4, 1) & (4, 2) & (4, 3) & (4, 4) & \cdots
\end{array}
$$

Let n be an arbitrarily given natural number. By the *n-th diagonal* of N^2, we mean the subset

$$
\begin{aligned}
D_n &= \{(i, j) \mid i + j = n + 1\} \\
    &= \{(1, n), (2, n - 1), \ldots, (n, 1)\}.
\end{aligned}
$$

The elements of D_n will be ordered as they are displayed above.

Now let us apply the counting process to N^2 following the diagonals in order. This can be illustrated by a diagram as follows.

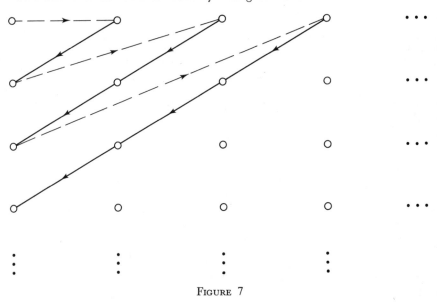

FIGURE 7

Here, the solid lines denote the diagonals D_2, D_3, D_4, etc.

For every natural number n, the nth diagonal D_n has n elements. It follows that the set

$$
D_1 \cup D_2 \cup \cdots \cup D_n
$$

consists of $n(n + 1)/2$ elements of N^2. Hence this counting process defines a bijective function $f : N^2 \to N$ given by

$$f(i, j) = \tfrac{1}{2}(i + j - 1)(i + j - 2) + i$$

for every element $(i, j) \in N^2$. This proves that N^2 is countable.‖

The following corollary is a direct consequence of (9.7) and (9.9).

COROLLARY 9.10. *For every natural number n, the Cartesian product*

$$F_n \times N$$

of the set $F_n = \{1, 2, \ldots, n\}$ *and the set N of all natural numbers is countable.*

PROPOSITION 9.11. *The union of a countable family of countable sets is countable.*

Proof. Let $\mathfrak{F} = \{X_\mu \mid \mu \in M\}$ denote any given countable family of countable sets. Then the set M is countable and, for each $\mu \in M$, X_μ is countable. If M is finite, it can be replaced by F_n for some $n \in N$; otherwise, M can be replaced by N. Assume that this has been done although we still use the symbol M.

Since X_μ is countable for each $\mu \in M$, it follows from (a) $\Rightarrow$ (b) of (9.5) that there exists a surjective function

$$f_\mu : N \rightarrow X_\mu$$

for every $\mu \in M$. Let X denote the union of the family $\mathfrak{F}$, and define a function

$$g : M \times N \rightarrow X$$

by taking

$$g(\mu, n) = f_\mu(n)$$

for every $\mu \in M$ and every $n \in N$. Since every f_μ is surjective, so obviously is g.

According to (9.9) and (9.10), $M \times N$ is countable. Hence, by (a) $\Rightarrow$ (b) of (9.5), there is a surjective function

$$h : N \rightarrow M \times N.$$

As a composition of surjective functions, the function

$$f = g \circ h : N \rightarrow X$$

is also surjective. By (b) $\Rightarrow$ (a) of (9.5), this proves that the union X of the family $\mathfrak{F}$ is countable.‖

COROLLARY 9.12. *The set Z of all integers is countable.*

Proof. Since Z is the union of two countable sets N and

$$L = \{0, -1, -2, \ldots, -n, \ldots\},$$

it is countable by (9.11).‖

COROLLARY 9.13.   *The set Q of all rational numbers is countable.*

Proof. For each natural number $m \in N$, let Q_m denote the set of all rational numbers which can be represented by fractions with m as the denominator. To prove that Q_m is countable, consider the function $g_m : Z \to Q_m$ defined by

$$g_m(n) = n/m$$

for every integer $n \in Z$. Obviously, g_m is surjective. Since Z is countable by (9.12), there exists a surjective function $h: N \to Z$. As a composition of surjective functions, the function

$$f_m = g_m \circ h : N \to Q_m$$

is surjective for every $m \in N$. By (b) $\Rightarrow$ (a) of (9.5), Q_m is countable for each $m \in N$. Since Q is the union of the family

$$\mathcal{F} = \{ Q_m \mid m \in N \},$$

it follows from (9.11) that Q is countable. ‖

PROPOSITION 9.14.   *The Cartesian product $X \times Y$ of any two countable sets X and Y is countable.*

Proof. Since X and Y are countable, there are surjective functions $f: N \to X$ and $g: N \to Y$. Define a function

$$h : N^2 \to X \times Y$$

by taking

$$h(m, n) = [f(m), g(n)]$$

for every $m \in N$ and every $n \in N$. Clearly h is surjective.
Since N^2 is countable by (9.9), there is a surjective function

$$j : N \to N^2.$$

As a composition of surjective functions, the function

$$k = h \circ j : N \to X \times Y$$

is surjective. By (b) $\Rightarrow$ (a) of (9.5), this implies that $X \times Y$ is countable. ‖

For an example of noncountable sets, we have the following proposition.

PROPOSITION 9.15.   *The unit interval I of real numbers is not countable.*

Proof. To prove by the indirect method, let us assume that the unit interval I is countable. Then, by (a) $\Rightarrow$ (b) of (9.5), there exists a surjective function

$$f : N \to I$$

from the set N of all natural numbers onto I.

In the decimal system, every real number $\alpha \epsilon I$ can be represented by

$$\alpha = \alpha_0.\alpha_1\alpha_2 \cdots \alpha_n \cdots$$

where $\alpha_0 = 0$ if $0 \leqslant \alpha < 1$ and $\alpha_0 = 1$ if $\alpha = 1$ while $0 \leqslant \alpha_n \leqslant 9$ for every $n \geqslant 1$. For each $m \epsilon N$, let us represent the real number $f(m) \epsilon I$ in this way, namely,

$$f(m) = \alpha_{m0}.\alpha_{m1}\alpha_{m2} \cdots \alpha_{mn} \cdots .$$

Define a real number

$$\beta = \beta_0.\beta_1\beta_2 \cdots \beta_n \cdots$$

of the unit interval I as follows: Let $\beta_0 = 0$. For each natural number n, set

$$\beta_n = \begin{cases} 1, & (\text{if } \alpha_{nn} \neq 1) \\ 2, & (\text{if } \alpha_{nn} = 1). \end{cases}$$

For each $n \epsilon N$, we have $\beta_n \neq \alpha_{nn}$ and hence $\beta \neq f(n)$. It follows that the real number β is not in the image $f(N)$. This contradicts our assumption that f is surjective and completes the proof of (9.15).‖

The following corollary is a direct consequence of (9.7) and (9.15).

COROLLARY 9.16. *The set R of all real numbers is not countable.*

EXERCISES

9A. Prove that the Cartesian product $X \times Y$ of any two finite sets X and Y is finite. Furthermore, if X has m elements and Y has n elements, then show that $X \times Y$ has mn elements.

9B. Prove that the union $X \cup Y$ and the intersection $X \cap Y$ of any two finite sets X and Y are finite. Let m, n, p, q denote the numbers of elements in X, Y, $X \cup Y$, $X \cap Y$, respectively. Prove the following relations:
  (a) $p \leqslant m + n$
  (b) $q \leqslant \text{Min}(m, n)$
  (c) $p + q = m + n$.

9C. Prove that every quotient set Q of a finite set X is finite. Furthermore, show that the number of elements in Q can never be greater than the number of elements in X.

9D. Prove that the union $F \cup G$ and the Cartesian product $F \times G$ of a finite set F and a countably infinite set G are countably infinite.

9E. Prove that the union $X \cup Y$ and the Cartesian product $X \times Y$ of any two countably infinite sets X and Y are countably infinite.

9F. By means of the exponential function $\exp : R \rightarrow P$ defined by $\exp(x) = e^x$ for every $x \in R$, show that the set R of all real numbers has the same cardinality as the set P of all positive real numbers.

9G. By means of the function $f : (0, 1) \rightarrow P$ defined on the open unit interval $(0, 1)$ by

$$f(x) = \begin{cases} x & \text{(if } 0 < x \leqslant \frac{1}{2}) \\ \dfrac{1}{4(1-x)} & \text{(if } \frac{1}{2} < x < 1), \end{cases}$$

prove that the open unit interval $(0, 1)$ has the same cardinality as the set P of all positive real numbers. Hence, R, P, and $(0, 1)$ have the same cardinality.

Chapter II: NUMBER SYSTEMS

In this chapter, we will rigorously present the classical construction of the number systems starting from the natural numbers characterized by the Peano postulates and ending with the complex numbers. Among the various definitions of real numbers, we will follow Cantor's method by using sequences of rational numbers. Rigorous constructions of the number systems are naturally complicated and intrinsically dull unless the reader is anxious to see how these numbers are logically defined. Our main purpose in this chapter is to provide those mathematics majors who are not happy with the intuitive descriptions of the number systems learned in high school or in calculus with the first chance to go through a rigorous study of the number systems and to lay a sound foundation for their further studies. Other readers may skip the whole chapter. Because of this, we will not introduce in this chapter any algebraic notion that will be used in the later chapters. On the other hand, we have managed to complete the job without explicitly using the terminology introduced in the later chapters.

1. NATURAL NUMBERS

After many years of studying arithmetic in schools, the student is well acquainted with the *natural numbers*, which are usually called *whole numbers* in daily life. Because of this fact, we will not try to give any philosophical or logical definition of these numbers.

As before, we will let N denote the set of all natural numbers. We mentioned in (I, §8) that N is well-ordered by the linear order $<$ which reads "is less than." Consequently, there exists a unique least natural number which is denoted by the symbol 1. Furthermore, for an arbitrary natural number $a \in N$, the subset

$$S(a) = \{x \in N \mid a < x\}$$

of N has a unique least number a^* which will be called the *successor* of the natural number a. In daily life, a^* is called the next whole number after a.

The successor of the natural number 1 is denoted by the symbol 2; the successor of the natural number 2 is denoted by the symbol 3; and so on. Hence the set N of all natural numbers together with its linear order $<$ can be represented as follows:

$$N = \{1, 2, 3, \ldots\}.$$

In terms of the concept "successor," the set N of natural numbers has the following five basic properties:

(P1) *1 is a natural number.*
(P2) *Every natural number a has a unique natural number a^* as its successor.*
(P3) *No natural number has 1 as its successor.*
(P4) *For arbitrary natural numbers a and b, $a^* = b^*$ implies $a = b$.*
(P5) *If a subset S of N contains 1 and the successor a^* of every $a \epsilon S$, then we have $S = N$.*

These properties of N are known as the *Peano postulates* of natural numbers. In fact, they essentially characterize the natural numbers except for their names.

The property **(P5)** of N is known as the *principle of complete induction*. It provides a basis for the *method of mathematical induction* frequently used in mathematical proofs and mathematical constructions. Numerous examples will be found in the sequel.

Because of **(P2)** and **(P3)**, we may define a function

$$\sigma : N \to N \backslash \{1\}$$

by setting $\sigma(a) = a^*$ for every $a \epsilon N$. This function σ will be called the *succession function* of natural numbers.

PROPOSITION 1.1.   *The succession function $\sigma : N \to N \backslash \{1\}$ of natural numbers is bijective and preserves the order $<$.*

Proof.   By the property **(P4)**, σ is clearly injective. To prove that σ is surjective, it suffices to show that the subset

$$S = \{1\} \cup \sigma(N)$$

of N is equal to N. For this purpose, we will apply the principle of complete induction as follows.

First, we have $1 \epsilon S$ by the definition of S. Next, let a denote any member of S. Then a is a natural number and we have

$$a^* = \sigma(a) \epsilon \sigma(N) \subset S.$$

Hence S contains a^*. By **(P5)**, this implies $S = N$. Therefore, σ is a bijective function.

To prove that σ preserves the order $<$, let us consider any two natural numbers a and b satisfying $a < b$. Then b is a member of the set

$$S(a) = \{x \in N \mid a < x\}.$$

Since a^* is the least number in $S(a)$, we have $a^* \leqslant b$. Since b^* is in $S(b)$, we have $b < b^*$. Hence we obtain

$$\sigma(a) = a^* < b^* = \sigma(b).$$

This proves that σ preserves the order $<$ and completes the proof (1.1).$\|$

By means of the properties **(P1)**–**(P5)**, we can precisely define *addition* and *multiplication* of natural numbers.

First let us define addition. For this purpose, let a denote any given natural number. We define the *sum* $a + 1$ of the natural numbers a and 1 by the formula

(A1) $$a + 1 = a^*,$$

where a^* denotes the successor of the natural number a. Now suppose that the *sum* $a + b$ of the given natural number a and some natural number b, such as 1, has been defined. We define the sum $a + b^*$ of a and the successor b^* of b by the formula

(A2) $$a + b^* = (a + b)^*.$$

In other words, the sum $a + b^*$ of a and b^* is defined to be the successor of the natural number $a + b$.

Now we claim that we have defined the *sum* $a + b$ of any two natural numbers a and b. To prove this, we will apply the principle of complete induction **(P5)**. For this purpose, let $A(a)$ denote the set of all natural numbers b such that $a + b$ is defined. By **(A1)**, $A(a)$ contains 1. By **(A2)**, $A(a)$ contains b^* for every $b \in A(a)$. It follows from **(P5)** that $A(a) = N$. Hence $a + b$ is defined for every $b \in N$. Since a is an arbitrary natural number, this proves our claim.

The above is an example of the *method of mathematical induction* applied in the construction of the sum $a + b$ of any two natural numbers a and b. This is a very important constructive method in mathematics, frequently known as the *inductive construction*.

Next, let us define multiplication by the method of inductive construction. For this purpose, let a denote any given natural number. We define the *product* $a1$ of the natural numbers a and 1 by the formula

(M1) $$a1 = a.$$

Now suppose that the *product ab* of the given natural number *a* and some natural number *b*, such as 1, has been defined. We define the product *ab** of *a* and the successor *b** of *b* by the formula

(**M2**) $$ab^* = ab + a.$$

Now we claim that we have defined the *product ab* of any two natural numbers *a* and *b*. To prove this, let $M(a)$ denote the set of all natural numbers such that *ab* is defined. By (**M1**), $M(a)$ contains 1. By (**M2**), $M(a)$ contains *b** for every $b \,\epsilon\, M(a)$. It follows from (**P5**) that $M(a) = N$. Hence *ab* is defined for every $b \,\epsilon\, N$. Since *a* is an arbitrary natural number, this proves our claim.

The student is expected to be acquainted with the basic properties of the natural numbers relating to addition and multiplication. They are given by the following theorem.

THEOREM 1.2.   *Let a, b, c, and d denote arbitrarily given natural numbers. Then the following statements are true:*

(**1**) *Commutative laws:*
$$a + b = b + a$$
$$ab = ba.$$

(**2**) *Associative laws:*
$$a + (b + c) = (a + b) + c$$
$$a(bc) = (ab)c.$$

(**3**) *Distributive law:*
$$a(b + c) = ab + ac.$$

(**4**) *Cancellation laws:*
$$a + b = a + c \quad \text{implies} \quad b = c$$
$$ab = ac \quad \text{implies} \quad b = c.$$

(**5**) *Order-preserving laws:*
$$a \leqslant b \quad \text{and} \quad c < d \quad \text{imply} \quad a + c < b + d$$
$$a \leqslant b \quad \text{and} \quad c < d \quad \text{imply} \quad ac < bd.$$

These laws for natural numbers are familiar to every college student. Besides, they can be proved by means of the properties (**P1**)–(**P5**), the definition of addition and multiplication, and the fact that the succession function σ preserves the order $<$. The proofs of these laws are left to the interested reader.

Next let us consider the possibility of subtraction in the set N of natural numbers. For this purpose, we have the following theorem.

THEOREM 1.3. *Let a and b denote any two given natural numbers. Then there exists a natural number c with $a + c = b$ iff $a < b$.*

Proof. Necessity. Let S denote the subset of N which consists of all $c \in N$ having the property that, for any two natural numbers a and b, $a + c = b$ implies $a < b$. According to the definition of

$$a + 1 = a^*,$$

the set S obviously contains the natural number 1. Now let c denote any given natural number in S, and consider any two natural numbers a and b satisfying

$$a + c^* = b.$$

Since $c + 1 = c^*$, this implies that

$$a^* + c = a + 1 + c = a + c + 1 = a + c^* = b.$$

Since $c \in S$, this implies $a < a^* < b$. By the transitivity of the order $<$, we have $a < b$. This proves $c^* \in S$. According to the property (**P5**) of natural numbers, we have $S = N$. This completes the necessity proof.

Sufficiency. Let a and b denote any two natural numbers satisfying $a < b$. Then b is a member of the set

$$S(a) = \{x \in N \mid a < x\}.$$

Because of the necessity part of the theorem, we may define a function

$$f : N \to S(a)$$

by setting $f(c) = a + c$ for every $c \in N$.

Since $b \in S(a)$, it suffices to prove that this function f is surjective. For this purpose, let us consider the sets

$$T(a) = \{x \in N \mid x \leqslant a\} = \{1, 2, \ldots, a\}$$
$$U = T(a) \cup f(N).$$

Obviously U contains the natural number 1. Next, let u denote any member of U. If $u < a$, then $u^* \leqslant a$ and hence

$$u^* \in T(a) \subset U.$$

If $u = a$, then $u^* = a^* = a + 1 = f(1)$ and hence

$$u^* \in f(N) \subset U.$$

If $u > a$, then u must belong to $f(N)$. It follows that there exists a natural number $c \in N$ with $u = f(c)$. This implies

$$u^* = u + 1 = f(c) + 1 = a + c + 1 = a + c^* = f(c^*).$$

Hence we also have
$$u^* \,\epsilon\, f(N) \subset U.$$
Consequently U always contains the successor u^* of u. According to the property (**P5**) of natural numbers, this implies $U = N$. Since
$$f(N) \subset S(a) \qquad S(a) \cap T(a) = \square,$$
it follows that $f(N) = S(a)$ and hence f is surjective.$\|$

COROLLARY 1.4. *For any two natural numbers a and b satisfying a $<$ b, there exists a unique natural number c such that*
$$a + c = b$$
holds. This natural number c is called the difference of the natural numbers b and a denoted by the symbol b $-$ a.

Proof. Because of (1.3), it remains to prove the uniqueness of the natural number c. For this purpose, let c and d denote any two natural numbers such that
$$a + c = b = a + d.$$
According to the cancellation law for addition in (1.2), this implies
$$c = d.$$
Hence the natural number c is unique and (1.4) is proved.$\|$

Because of (1.3) and (1.4), the *difference* $b - a$ of two natural numbers b and a is defined in the system N of natural numbers iff $a < b$ holds.

Now let us consider the possibility of division and factorization in the set N of natural numbers. For this purpose, let b denote an arbitrarily given natural number.

A natural number a is said to be a *divisor* of the given natural number b iff there exists a natural number c such that $ac = b$. In this case, b is said to be *divisible* by a and is also called a *multiple* of a.

PROPOSITION 1.5. *For any divisor a of a given natural number b, there exists a unique natural number c such that*
$$ac = b$$
holds. This natural number c is called the quotient of the natural number b over a, denoted by the symbol b/a.

Proof. Since the existence of c is a consequence of the definition, it remains to prove the uniqueness of c. For this purpose, let c and d denote any two natural numbers such that
$$ac = b = ad.$$

According to the cancellation law for multiplication in (1.2), this implies

$$c = d.$$

Hence the natural number c is unique and (1.5) is proved.‖

Thus the *quotient* b/a of a natural number b over a natural number a is defined in the system N of natural numbers iff b is divisible by a.

A natural number $p > 1$ is said to be *prime* iff p has no divisor other than 1 and p itself. Two natural numbers a and b are said to be *relatively prime* iff they have no common divisor other than 1.

The first few prime natural numbers are

$$2, 3, 5, 7, 11, 13, 17, 19, 23, 29, 31, 37, \ldots.$$

EXERCISES

1A. Let a, b, c, and d denote arbitrary natural numbers. Prove the following equalities:
   (i) $(a + b)c = ac + bc$
   (ii) $(a + b)(c + d) = (ac + bc) + (ad + bd)$
   (iii) $a(b + c)d = (ab)d + a(cd)$.

1B. For arbitrary natural numbers a and n, the nth power a^n of a is defined inductively by

$$a^1 = a \qquad a^{n+1} = a^n a.$$

Prove the following equalities:
   (i) $a^m a^n = a^{m+n}$
   (ii) $(a^m)^n = a^{mn}$
   (iii) $(ab)^n = a^n b^n$.

1C. Prove the following equalities by means of mathematical induction:
   (i) $1 + 2 + 3 + \cdots + n = n(n + 1)/2$
   (ii) $1^2 + 2^2 + 3^2 + \cdots + n^2 = n(n + 1)(2n + 1)/6$
   (iii) $1^3 + 2^3 + 3^3 + \cdots + n^3 = [n(n + 1)/2]^2$.

1D. Let a and b denote any two natural numbers such that a is not a divisor of b. Prove that there exist uniquely determined natural numbers q and r satisfying

$$b = aq + r \qquad (1 \leqslant r < a).$$

1E. A natural number d is said to be a *greatest common divisor* (g.c.d.) of two given natural numbers a and b iff d is a common divisor of a and

b and is a multiple of every common divisor of a and b. Prove that any two given natural numbers a and b have a unique greatest common divisor d. In particular, the given natural numbers a and b are relatively prime iff their greatest common divisor is 1.

1F. A natural number m is said to be a *least common multiple* (l.c.m.) of two given natural numbers a and b iff m is a common multiple of a and b and every common multiple of a and b is a multiple of m. Prove that any two natural numbers a and b have a unique least common divisor m and that m is equal to quotient ab/d of their product ab over their greatest common divisor d.

1G. By the method of mathematical induction, prove that the subset $F_n = \{1, 2, \ldots, n\}$ of N is finite for every $n \in N$. Establish the following statements:

  (i) The union $X \cup Y$ of two finite sets X and Y is finite.

  (ii) If X is an infinite set, then there exists an injective function $f: N \to X$ from the set N of natural numbers into X.

1H. Prove the statements (1)–(5) in the theorem (1.2).

2. INTEGERS

As we have seen in the preceding section, the difference $b - a$ of two natural numbers a and b is defined in the system N of natural numbers iff $a < b$. In order to define the difference $b - a$ for every pair of natural numbers a and b, one has to create *zero* and *negative integers*. In a rigorous and elegant approach, we shall construct, by the method of forming Cartesian product and quotient set, a new system Z of numbers, called *integers*, and identify the natural numbers N as a part of Z, namely, the *positive integers*.

For this purpose, let us consider the Cartesian square

$$N^2 = N \times N$$

of the set N of natural numbers. The members of N^2 are the ordered pairs (a, b) of natural numbers. Define a relation $\sim$ in N^2 by setting

$$(a, b) \sim (c, d) \quad \text{iff} \quad a + d = b + c$$

for any two members (a, b) and (c, d) of N^2.

LEMMA 2.1.   *The relation* $\sim$ *in* N^2 *is an equivalence relation.*

Proof.   We have to verify that $\sim$ is reflexive, symmetric, and transitive.

To prove that $\sim$ is reflexive, let (a, b) denote any member of N^2. According to the commutative law for addition of natural numbers, we have $a + b = b + a$. By definition, this implies $(a, b) \sim (a, b)$. Hence $\sim$ is reflexive.

To prove that $\sim$ is symmetric, let (a, b) and (c, d) denote any two members of N^2 such that $(a, b) \sim (c, d)$ holds. By definition, this implies $a + d = b + c$. Because of the commutative law for addition of natural numbers, we have $c + b = d + a$. By definition, this implies $(c, d) \sim (a, b)$. Hence $\sim$ is symmetric.

To prove that $\sim$ is transitive, let (a, b), (c, d), and (e, f) denote any three members of N^2 such that $(a, b) \sim (c, d)$ and $(c, d) \sim (e, f)$ hold. By definition, we have $a + d = b + c$ and $c + f = d + e$. Adding f to the former equality and b to the latter, we obtain

$$d + a + f = b + c + f = d + b + e$$

after making use of the commutativity and the associativity of addition of natural numbers. From the cancellation law for addition of natural numbers, it follows that $a + f = b + e$. By definition, this implies $(a, b) \sim (e, f)$. Hence $\sim$ is transitive.$\|$

According to (I, §8), this equivalence relation $\sim$ in N^2 defines a quotient set of N^2 which will be denoted by

$$Z = N^2/\sim.$$

The members of Z are called *integers*. Thus the integers are the equivalence classes in N^2 with respect to $\sim$.

LEMMA 2.2. *Let (a, b) and (c, d) denote any two members of N^2 such that*

$$(a, b) \sim (c, d)$$

holds. Then the following three statements are true:

(i) $a < b$ *iff* $c < d$
(ii) $a = b$ *iff* $c = d$
(iii) $a > b$ *iff* $c > d$.

Proof. Since $(a, b) \sim (c, d)$ holds, we have the following equality:

(0) $$a + d = b + c.$$

To prove (i), let us assume $a < b$. By (1.3), there exists a natural number x satisfying $a + x = b$. Adding x to the equality (0), we obtain

$$b + d = a + x + d = b + c + x.$$

By the cancellation law for addition of natural numbers, this implies $d = c + x$. Then it follows from (1.3) that $c < d$. This proves that $a < b$ implies $c < d$. Similarly, one can prove that $c < d$ implies $a < b$.

To prove (ii), let us assume $a = b$. Then it follows from the cancellation law that the equality (0) implies $c = d$. This proves that $a = b$ implies $c = d$. Similarly, one can prove that $c = d$ implies $a = b$.

The proof of (iii) is similar to that of (i) and hence it is omitted.$\|$

Now let ξ denote an arbitrarily given integer. By definition, ξ is an equivalence class of ordered pairs of natural numbers. Because of (2.2), it is satisfactory to make the following definitions.

The integer ξ is said to be *positive* iff it contains an ordered pair $(a, b) \in N^2$ with $a < b$. The integer ξ is said to be *zero* iff it contains an ordered pair $(a, b) \in N^2$ with $a = b$. Finally, the integer ξ is said to be *negative* iff it contains an ordered pair $(a, b) \in N^2$ with $a > b$.

PROPOSITION 2.3.   *In the system Z of integers, there is a unique zero which will be denoted by the symbol 0.*

Proof.   The existence of a zero in Z is obvious since the integer which contains the pair $(1, 1) \in N^2$ is zero by definition.

To prove the uniqueness, let ξ and η denote any two zeroes in Z. Then, by definition, there exist $(a, b) \in \xi$ and $(c, d) \in \eta$ with $a = b$ and $c = d$. It follows that

$$a + d = b + c$$

holds and hence we have $(a, b) \sim (c, d)$. Since ξ and η are equivalence classes with respect to $\sim$, this implies $\xi = \eta$.$\|$

The following proposition is a direct consequence of the definition.

PROPOSITION 2.4.   *For an arbitrary integer $\xi \in Z$, one and only one of the following three statements is true:*

(i)   *ξ is positive*
(ii) *$\xi = 0$*
(iii) *ξ is negative.*

Next, we shall define a relation $<$ in the set Z of integers. For this purpose, let us first establish the following lemma.

LEMMA 2.5.   *Let (a, b), (a', b'), (c, d), and $(c'\ d')$ denote arbitrarily given members of N^2 satisfying $(a, b) \sim (a', b')$ and $(c, d) \sim (c', d')$. Then we have*

$$b + c < a + d \quad \text{iff} \quad b' + c' < a' + d'.$$

Proof. Because of the symmetry of $\sim$, it suffices to prove that $b + c < a + d$ implies $b' + c' < a' + d'$. Hence we assume

(i) $$b + c < a + d.$$

Since $(a, b) \sim (a', b')$ and $(c, d) \sim (c', d')$, we have the following two equalities:

(ii) $$a + b' = b + a'$$
(iii) $$d + c' = c + d'.$$

Adding **(i)**, **(ii)**, and **(iii)**, we obtain

(iv) $$s + b' + c' < s + a' + d'$$

where $s = a + b + c + d$. By (4) and (5) of (1.2), one can deduce from **(iv)** the inequality

$$b' + c' < a' + d'.$$

This completes the proof of (2.5).$\|$

Now let ξ and η denote any two given integers. Because of (2.5), we may define a relation $<$ in $\mathcal{Z}$ by setting

$$\xi < \eta$$

iff there exist $(a, b) \in \xi$ and $(c, d) \in \eta$ such that $b + c < a + d$ hold.

PROPOSITION 2.6. *The relation $<$ in the set $\mathcal{Z}$ of integers is a linear order.*

Proof. To establish the transitivity of the relation $<$, let us consider any three given integers ξ, η, ζ such that $\xi < \eta$ and $\eta < \zeta$ hold. By definition and (2.5), there exist $(a, b) \in \xi$, $(c, d) \in \eta$, and $(e, f) \in \zeta$ such that the following two inequalities are true:

(i) $$b + c < a + d$$
(ii) $$d + e < c + f.$$

Adding **(i)** and **(ii)**, we obtain

(iii) $$(d + c) + b + e < (d + c) + a + f.$$

By (4) and (5) of (1.2), one can deduce from **(iii)** the inequality

$$b + e < a + f.$$

This implies $\xi < \zeta$. Hence $<$ is a partial order in $\mathcal{Z}$.

To prove that $<$ is a linear order in $\mathcal{Z}$, let ξ and η denote any two integers. Pick $(a, b) \in \xi$ and $(c, d) \in \eta$. By the property of $<$ in $\mathcal{N}$, one and only one of the following three relations

$$b + c < a + d, \qquad b + c = a + d, \qquad b + c > a + d$$

is true. By definition, this implies that one and only one of the following three relations

$$\xi < \eta, \qquad \xi = \eta, \qquad \xi > \eta$$

is true. Thus the conditions (**L1**) and (**L2**) in (I, §8) are satisfied. This proves that $<$ is a linear order in $\mathcal{Z}$.‖

In the preceding proof, we have also established the following corollary.

COROLLARY 2.7.   *For any two integers ξ and η, one and only one of the following three statements is true:*

$$\text{(i) } \xi < \eta, \qquad \text{(ii) } \xi = \eta, \qquad \text{(iii) } \xi > \eta.$$

The following proposition is a direct consequence of the definitions.

PROPOSITION 2.8.   *The following two statements are true for every integer ξ:*

(**i**)   *ξ is positive iff $\xi > 0$*
(**ii**)   *ξ is negative iff $\xi < 0$.*

For convenience of further study on the integers in the remainder of this section, we shall let

$$p : \mathcal{N}^2 \to \mathcal{Z}$$

denote the *natural projection* of $\mathcal{N}^2$ onto its quotient set $\mathcal{Z}$. As defined in (I, §8), p is a surjective function sending each pair $(a, b) \in \mathcal{N}^2$ to the equivalence class $p(a, b) \in \mathcal{Z}$ which contains the pair (a, b).

To define addition and multiplication of integers, let ξ and η denote any two given integers. By definition, ξ and η are equivalence classes in $\mathcal{N}^2$ with respect to $\sim$. Choose $(a, b) \in \xi$ and $(c, d) \in \eta$. Then it is straightforward to verify that the integers $p(a + c, b + d)$ and $p(ad + bc, ac + bd)$ do not depend on the choice of the pairs (a, b) and (c, d) from the equivalence classes ξ and η. Hence we may define the *sum* $\xi + \eta$ and the *product* $\xi\eta$ by taking

$$\xi + \eta = p(a + c, b + d)$$
$$\xi\eta = p(ad + bc, ac + bd).$$

Since addition and multiplication of integers have been defined above, it is easy to verify the laws stated in the following theorem.

THEOREM 2.9.   *Let α, β, γ, and δ denote arbitrarily given integers. Then the following statements are true:*

(**1**)   *Commutative laws:*
$$\alpha + \beta = \beta + \alpha$$
$$\alpha\beta = \beta\alpha.$$

(2) *Associative laws:*

$$\alpha + (\beta + \gamma) = (\alpha + \beta) + \gamma$$
$$\alpha(\beta\gamma) = (\alpha\beta)\gamma.$$

(3) *Distributive law:*

$$\alpha(\beta + \gamma) = \alpha\beta + \alpha\gamma.$$

(4) *Cancellation laws:*

$$\alpha + \beta = \alpha + \gamma \quad implies \quad \beta = \gamma$$
$$\alpha \neq 0 \quad and \quad \alpha\beta = \alpha\gamma \quad imply \quad \beta = \gamma.$$

(5) *Order-preserving laws:*

$$\alpha \leqslant \beta \quad and \quad \gamma < \delta \quad imply \quad \alpha + \gamma < \beta + \delta$$
$$0 < \alpha \leqslant \beta \quad and \quad 0 < \gamma < \delta \quad imply \quad \alpha\gamma < \beta\delta.$$

The integer 0 plays a special role in addition and multiplication as given by the following proposition.

PROPOSITION 2.10. *For every integer ξ, we have $\xi + 0 = \xi$ and $\xi 0 = 0$.*

Proof. Let $(a, b) \in \xi$ and $(c, d) \in 0$. Then we have $c = d$. This implies

$$(a, b) \sim (a + c, b + d)$$
$$ad + bc = ac + bd.$$

Hence we obtain $\xi + 0 = \xi$ and $\xi 0 = 0.\|$

In order to study subtraction, let us first define the *negation*, $-\xi$, of any given integer ξ. We propose this terminology because the word "negative" has been used for another meaning.

Consider an arbitrarily given integer ξ and choose a pair $(a, b) \in \xi$. Obviously, the integer $p(b, a)$ does not depend on the choice of the pair (a, b) from the equivalence class ξ. Hence we may define the *negation* of the integer ξ to be the integer

$$-\xi = p(b, a).$$

The following proposition can be easily established.

PROPOSITION 2.11. *For arbitrary integers ξ and η, the following six statements are true:*

(i) $\quad -(-\xi) = \xi$
(ii) $\quad -\xi = 0 \quad iff \quad \xi = 0$
(iii) $\quad -\xi > 0 \quad iff \quad \xi < 0$
(iv) $\quad -\xi < 0 \quad iff \quad \xi > 0$
(v) $\quad (-\xi)(-\eta) = \xi\eta$
(vi) $\quad (-\xi)\eta = -(\xi\eta) = \xi(-\eta).$

By the *negation function* of $\mathbb{Z}$, we mean the function

$$r:\mathbb{Z} \to \mathbb{Z}$$

defined by $r(\xi) = -\xi$ for every $\xi \in \mathbb{Z}$. By **(i)** of (2.11), the composition $r \circ r$ is the identity function on $\mathbb{Z}$. Hence it follows from (I, 6.4) that r is bijective and is its own inverse. By **(ii)**–**(iv)** of (2.11), r sends the positive integers bijectively onto the negative integers, and vice versa.

To define subtraction, let ξ and η denote arbitrarily given integers. Then we define their *difference*, $\eta - \xi$, by taking

$$\eta - \xi = \eta + (-\xi).$$

PROPOSITION 2.12. *For any two integers ξ and η, there exists a unique integer ζ such that $\xi + \zeta = \eta$. Furthermore, we have $\zeta = \eta - \xi$.*

Proof. Choose $(a, b) \in \xi$ and $(c, d) \in \eta$. Then we have $-\xi = p(b, a)$ and hence

$$\eta - \xi = \eta + (-\xi) = p(c + b, d + a)$$
$$\xi + (\eta - \xi) = p(a + c + b, b + d + a) = p(c, d) = \eta.$$

This establishes existence. To prove uniqueness, let ζ denote any integer satisfying $\xi + \zeta = \eta$. Then we have

$$\xi + \zeta = \xi + (\eta - \xi).$$

According to the cancellation law for addition of integers, this implies $\zeta = \eta - \xi.\|$

In particular, if we take $\eta = 0$, then we have

$$\zeta = 0 - \xi = 0 + (-\xi) = -\xi.$$

Hence we obtain the following corollary of (2.12).

COROLLARY 2.13. *For any given integer ξ, we have*

$$\xi - \xi = \xi + (-\xi) = 0.$$

Now we will identify the natural numbers N with the positive integers. For this purpose, we define a function

$$j:N \to \mathbb{Z}$$

by taking $j(x) = p(1, 1 + x)$ for every $x \in N$.

PROPOSITION 2.14. *The function $j:N \to \mathbb{Z}$ is injective and its image $j(N)$ in $\mathbb{Z}$ is the set of all positive integers. Furthermore, j preserves order, addition, and multiplication; that is, for any two natural numbers a and b, the following three statements are true:*

(**i**) $a < b$ *implies* $j(a) < j(b)$
(**ii**) $j(a + b) = j(a) + j(b)$
(**iii**) $j(ab) = j(a)j(b).$

Proof. To prove that j is injective, let x and y denote any two natural numbers such that $j(x) = j(y)$. This implies

$$(1, 1 + x) \sim (1, 1 + y).$$

It follows from the definition of $\sim$ that

$$1 + 1 + x = 1 + 1 + y.$$

According to the cancellation law for addition of natural numbers, this implies $x = y$. Hence j is injective.

Since $1 < 1 + x$, it follows that $j(x)$ is a positive integer for every $x \in \mathcal{N}$.

Conversely, let ξ denote any positive integer. We will prove the existence of a natural number x such that $j(x) = \xi$. For this purpose, we will first prove that ξ contains a pair of the form $(1, w)$. Choose any pair $(a, b) \in \xi$. If $a = 1$, (a, b) is already of the form $(1, w)$ with $w = b$. If $a > 1$, then (1.3) assures the existence of a natural number c satisfying $1 + c = a$. Since ξ is positive, we have $c < a < b$. Hence there exists a natural number w satisfying $b = w + c$. Thus we obtain

$$(a, b) = (1 + c, w + c) \sim (1, w).$$

This proves that ξ contains a pair of the form $(1, w)$.

Since ξ is positive, we have $1 < w$. According to (1.3), there exists a natural number x satisfying $w = 1 + x$. Hence we obtain

$$j(x) = p(1, 1 + x) = p(1, w) = \xi.$$

This proves that the image $j(\mathcal{N})$ in $\mathcal{Z}$ is the set of all positive integers.

The verifications of the statements (**i**), (**ii**), and (**iii**) are straightforward and hence omitted.‖

The proposition (2.14) shows us that there is practically no difference between the natural numbers and the positive integers. Because of this, we may identify them; in other words, we may denote the positive integer $j(x)$ simply by the natural number x itself. This having been done, the positive integers are

$$1, 2, 3, 4, \ldots, n, \ldots.$$

On the other hand, since the negation function r sends the positive integers bijectively onto the negative integers, the latter can be uniquely denoted by

$$-1, -2, -3, -4, \ldots, -n, \ldots.$$

Therefore, the set $\mathcal{Z}$ of integers can be exhibited as follows:

$$\mathcal{Z} = \{\ldots, -4, -3, -2, -1, 0, 1, 2, 3, 4, \ldots\}.$$

After these identifications, we have the following proposition concerning the natural projection $p : \mathcal{N}^2 \to \mathcal{Z}$.

PROPOSITION 2.15.   *For every pair* (a, b) *of natural numbers, we have*

$$p(a, b) = b - a \in \mathcal{Z}.$$

Proof.   Because of the definitions, we have

$$
\begin{aligned}
p(a, b) &= p(2 + a, 2 + b) \\
        &= p(1, 1 + b) + p(1 + a, 1) \\
        &= p(1, 1 + b) - p(1, 1 + a) \\
        &= j(b) - j(a) = b - a.
\end{aligned}
$$

This proves (2.15).$\|$

This is actually what we wanted when we started the construction of the integers. Hereafter, since we have already constructed the integers and have identified the natural numbers with the positive integers, it is no longer necessary to use lower case Greek letters to denote integers.

In (2.12), we have seen that subtraction is uniquely defined in the system $\mathcal{Z}$ of integers. To conclude the present section, we will study the possibility of division in $\mathcal{Z}$. For this purpose, let us first define the *absolute value* $|x|$ of an arbitrarily given integer x by setting

$$
|x| = \begin{cases} x & \text{(if } x > 0), \\ 0 & \text{(if } x = 0), \\ -x & \text{(if } x < 0). \end{cases}
$$

Then one can easily verify the following proposition.

PROPOSITION 2.16.   *For arbitrarily given integers* x *and* y, *the following three statements are true:*

(i) $|-x| = |x|$

(ii) $|xy| = |x| |y|$

(iii) $|(|x| - |y|)| \leqslant |x + y| \leqslant |x| + |y|.$

Now let a and b denote any two given integers. We shall say that a is a *divisor* of b iff there exists an integer c such that $ac = b$. In this case, b is said to be *divisible* by a and is also called a *multiple* of a. The integer 0 plays an exceptional role in the study of division; in fact, it has the properties described by the following proposition.

PROPOSITION 2.17. *Every integer is a divisor of 0, and 0 can never be a divisor of any nonzero integer.*

Proof. Let a denote an arbitrary integer. Since $a0 = 0$, it follows that a is a divisor of 0. Next, let b denote any nonzero integer. Since

$$0c = 0 \neq b$$

holds for every integer c, it follows that 0 is not a divisor of b.‖

Because of (2.17), it remains to study nonzero integers. The divisibility of nonzero integers reduces to that of natural numbers; in fact, we have the following proposition.

PROPOSITION 2.18. *For any two given nonzero integers a and b, a is a divisor of b iff $| a |$ is a divisor of $| b |$.*

Proof. Necessity. Assume that a is a divisor of b. By definition, there exists an integer c such that $ac = b$ holds. According to (2.16), this implies $| a | | c | = | b |$. Hence $| a |$ is a divisor of $| b |$.

Sufficiency. Assume that $| a |$ is a divisor of $| b |$. Then there exists a (positive) integer c such that $| a | c = | b |$. From the definition of the absolute values $| a |$ and $| b |$, one can easily see that

$$b = \begin{cases} ac, & (\text{if } ab > 0) \\ -ac, & (\text{if } ab < 0) \end{cases}$$

holds. Hence a is a divisor of b. ‖

PROPOSITION 2.19. *Let $a \neq 0$ and b denote given integers. If b is divisible by a, then there exists a unique integer c satisfying $ac = b$.*

Proof. The existence of the integer c follows from the definition of divisibility. The uniqueness of the integer c is a consequence of the cancellation law for multiplication in (2.9).‖

The unique integer c in (2.19) is called the *quotient* of b over a and is denoted by b/a. Obviously $b/a = 0$ iff $b = 0$. In case $b \neq 0$, we have

$$b/a = \begin{cases} | b |/| a |, & (\text{if } ab > 0) \\ -(| b |/| a |), & (\text{if } ab < 0). \end{cases}$$

Thus the quotient b/a is defined in Z, iff $a \neq 0$ and b is divisible by a.

EXERCISES

2A. Let a, b, c denote integers. Prove the following statements:
  (i) $a < b$ implies $-a > -b$
  (ii) $a < b$ and $c < 0$ imply $ac > bc$.

2B. Let d denote the greatest common divisor of any two given positive integers a and b. Prove that there exist two integers p and q such that $d = pa + qb$ holds.

2C. Let p denote a prime natural number. Prove that p is a divisor of the product ab of two natural numbers a and b iff p is a divisor of a or b.

2D. Let x denote any natural number greater than 1. Prove that x can be expressed as a product

$$x = x_1 x_2 \cdots x_n$$

of a finite number of prime divisors $x_1, x_2, \ldots, x_n$ of x. The expression of x is unique except for the arrangement of the prime factors $x_1, x_2, \ldots, x_n$.

2E. Prove the countability of the set Z of integers by using the definition of Z as a quotient set of $N^2 = N \times N$.

2F. Consider the Cartesian square $Z^2 = Z \times Z$ and define a relation $\sim$ in Z^2 by setting $(a, b) \sim (c, d)$ iff $a + d = b + c$. Prove that $\sim$ is an equivalence relation in Z^2 and denote the quotient set by $W = Z^2/\sim$. Define a linear order, addition, and multiplication in W precisely as in the text for Z. Consider the function $h : Z^2 \to Z$ defined by $h(a, b) = b - a$ for every $(a, b) \in Z^2$. Prove that the inverse images $h^{-1}(x)$, $x \in Z$ are precisely the members of W. Hence h induces a bijective function $k : W \to Z$. Verify that k preserves order, sum, and product. Thus there is no essential difference between W and Z. This shows that this process, applied on Z as on N, does not lead to a larger system of numbers.

3. RATIONAL NUMBERS

As we have seen in the preceding section, the quotient b/a of two integers $a \neq 0$ and b is defined iff a is a divisor of b. In order to define the quotient b/a for every pair of integers $a \neq 0$ and b, one has to create *fractions*. In a rigorous and elegant approach as in the last section, we shall construct, by the method of forming a Cartesian product and quotient set, a new system Q of numbers, called *rational numbers*, and identify the integers Z as a part of Q.

For this purpose, let $Y = Z \setminus \{0\}$ and consider the Cartesian product

$$X = Y \times Z.$$

The members of X are the ordered pairs (a, b) of integers with $a \neq 0$. Define a relation $\sim$ in X by setting

$$(a, b) \sim (c, d) \quad \text{iff} \quad ad = bc$$

for any two members (a, b) and (c, d) of X.

LEMMA 3.1. *The relation $\sim$ in X is an equivalence relation.*

Proof. We have to verify that $\sim$ is reflexive, symmetric, and transitive.

To prove that $\sim$ is reflexive, let (a, b) denote any member of X. According to the commutative law for multiplication of integers, we have $ab = ba$. By definition, this implies $(a, b) \sim (a, b)$. Hence $\sim$ is reflexive.

To prove that $\sim$ is symmetric, let (a, b) and (c, d) denote any two members of X such that $(a, b) \sim (c, d)$ holds. By definition, this implies $ad = bc$. Because of the commutative law for multiplication of integers, we have $cb = da$. By definition, this implies $(c, d) \sim (a, b)$. Hence $\sim$ is symmetric.

To prove that $\sim$ is transitive, let (a, b), (c, d), and (e, f) denote any three members of X such that $(a, b) \sim (c, d)$ and $(c, d) \sim (e, f)$ hold. By definition, we have $ad = bc$ and $cf = de$. Multiplying the former by e and the latter by a, we obtain

$$caf = ade = cbe$$

after making use of the commutativity and associativity of multiplication of integers. Since $c \neq 0$, it follows from the cancellation law for multiplication of integers that $af = be$. By definition, this implies $(a, b) \sim (e, f)$. Hence $\sim$ is transitive.‖

According to (I, §8), this equivalence relation $\sim$ in X defines a quotient set of X which will be denoted by

$$Q = X/\sim.$$

The members of Q are called *rational numbers*. Thus the rational numbers are the equivalence classes in X with respect to $\sim$.

A member (a, b) of the set X is said to be *regular* iff $a > 0$.

LEMMA 3.2. *Every rational number contains a regular member of X.*

Proof. Let ξ denote any rational number. By definition, ξ is an equivalence class in X with respect to $\sim$. Choose a member $(a, b) \in \xi$. Since $(a, b) \sim (-a, -b)$ is obvious, we have $(-a, -b) \in \xi$. Since $a \neq 0$, we have $a > 0$ or $-a > 0$. Hence one of the two members (a, b) and $(-a, -b)$ is regular. This proves (3.2).‖

LEMMA 3.3.   *Let* (a, b) *and* (c, d) *denote any two regular members of* X
such that

$$(a, b) \sim (c, d)$$

holds. Then the following three statements are true:

(i) $b = 0$ *iff* $d = 0$
(ii) $b > 0$ *iff* $d > 0$
(iii) $b < 0$ *iff* $d < 0$.

Proof.   Since $(a, b) \sim (c, d)$ holds, we have the following equality:

(0) $ad = bc.$

Since (a, b) and (c, d) are regular members of X, we have $a > 0$ and
$c > 0$. Then the statements (i), (ii), and (iii) are direct consequences
of the equality (0).‖

Now let ξ denote an arbitrarily given rational number. Because of
(3.2) and (3.3), it is satisfactory to make the following definitions.

The rational number ξ is said to be *positive* iff it contains a regular
member (a, b) of X with $b > 0$. The rational number ξ is said to be *zero*
iff it contains a regular member (a, b) of X with $b = 0$. Finally, the
rational number ξ is said to be *negative* iff it contains a regular member
(a, b) of X with $b < 0$.

PROPOSITION 3.4.   *In the system* Q *of rational numbers, there is a unique
zero.*

Proof.   The existence of a zero in Q follows from the fact that the
rational number which contains the regular member $(1, 0)$ of X is a
zero by definition.

The uniqueness of zero in Q follows from the fact that $(a, b) \sim (1, 0)$
holds iff $b = 0$.‖

This unique zero in Q will be denoted by θ until otherwise stated.
In fact, θ is the subset of X defined by

$$\theta = \{(a, b) \, \epsilon \, X \mid b = 0\}.$$

The following proposition is a direct consequence of the definition.

PROPOSITION 3.5.   *For any rational number* $\xi \, \epsilon \, Q$, *one and only one of the
following three statements is true:*

(i) ξ *is positive*
(ii) ξ *is zero*
(iii) ξ *is negative.*

Next, we shall define a relation $<$ in the set Q of rational numbers. For this purpose, let us first state the following lemma which is not difficult to verify.

LEMMA 3.6. *Let* (a, b), (a', b'), (c, d), *and* (c', d') *denote regular members of* X *satisfying* $(a, b) \sim (a', b')$ *and* $(c, d) \sim (c', d')$. *Then we have*

$$bc < ad \quad iff \quad b'c' < a'd'.$$

Now let ξ and η denote any two given rational numbers. Because of (3.6), we may define a relation $<$ in Q by setting

$$\xi < \eta$$

iff there exist regular members $(a, b) \, \epsilon \, \xi$ and $(c, d) \, \epsilon \, \eta$ such that $bc < ad$.

PROPOSITION 3.7. *The relation* $<$ *in the set* Q *of rational numbers is a linear order.*

The proof of (3.7) is not difficult and hence is left to students.

The following two propositions are direct consequences of the definitions.

PROPOSITION 3.8. *For any two rational numbers* ξ *and* η, *one and only one of the following three statements is true:*

(i) $\xi < \eta$, **(ii)** $\xi = \eta$, **(iii)** $\xi > \eta$.

PROPOSITION 3.9. *The following two statements are true for every rational number* ξ:

(i) ξ *is positive iff* $\xi > \theta$
(ii) ξ *is negative iff* $\xi < \theta$.

For convenience of further study in the remainder of this section, we shall let

$$p : X \to Q$$

denote the *natural projection* of X onto its quotient set Q. As defined in (I, §8), p is a surjective function sending each pair $(a, b) \, \epsilon \, X$ to the equivalence class $p(a, b) \, \epsilon \, Q$ which contains the pair (a, b).

To define addition and multiplication of rational numbers, let ξ and η denote any two given rational numbers. By definition, ξ and η are equivalence classes in X with respect to $\sim$. Choose $(a, b) \, \epsilon \, \xi$ and $(c, d) \, \epsilon \, \eta$. Then it is straightforward to verify that the rational numbers $p(ac, ad + bc)$ and $p(ac, bd)$ do not depend on the choice of the pairs (a, b)

and (c, d) from the given equivalence classes ξ and η. Hence we may define the *sum* $\xi + \eta$ and the *product* $\xi\eta$ by taking

$$\xi + \eta = p(ac, ad + bc)$$
$$\xi\eta = p(ac, bd).$$

Having defined addition and multiplication as above, one can easily verify the following theorem.

THEOREM 3.10.   *Let* α, β, γ, *and* δ *denote arbitrarily given rational numbers. Then we have the laws* (1)–(5) *in* (2.9) *with* 0 *replaced by* θ.

The rational number θ plays a special role in addition and multiplication as given by the following proposition.

PROPOSITION 3.11.   *For every rational number* ξ, *we have* $\xi + \theta = \xi$ *and* $\xi\theta = \theta$.

Proof.   Let $(a, b) \in \xi$ and $(c, d) \in \theta$. Then we have $d = 0$. This implies

$$(a, b) \sim (ac, ad + bc)$$
$$bd = 0.$$

Hence we obtain $\xi + \theta = \xi$ and $\xi\theta = \theta.\|$

In order to study subtraction, let us first define the *negation*, $-\xi$, of any given rational number ξ. For this purpose, choose a pair $(a, b) \in \xi$. Obviously, the rational number $p(a, -b)$ does not depend on the choice of the pair (a, b) from the equivalence class ξ. Hence we may define the *negation* of the rational number ξ to be the rational number

$$-\xi = p(a, -b).$$

The following proposition can be easily verified.

PROPOSITION 3.12.   *For arbitrary rational numbers* ξ *and* η, *we have the statements* (**i**)–(**vi**) *in* (2.11) *with* 0 *replaced by* θ.

By the *negation function* of Q, we mean the function

$$r: Q \to Q$$

defined by $r(\xi) = -\xi$ for every $\xi \in Q$. One can easily verify that the composition $r \circ r$ is the identity function on Q. Hence it follows from (I, 6.4) that r is bijective and is its own inverse. By (**ii**)–(**iv**) of (3.12), r sends the positive rational numbers bijectively onto the negative rational numbers, and vice versa.

To define subtraction, let ξ and η denote arbitrarily given rational numbers. Then we define their *difference* $\eta - \xi$ by taking

$$\eta - \xi = \eta + (-\xi).$$

The following proposition can be easily verified.

PROPOSITION 3.13. *For any two rational numbers ξ and η, there exists a unique rational number ζ such that $\xi + \zeta = \eta$. Furthermore, we have $\zeta = \eta - \xi$.*

In particular, if we take $\eta = \theta$, then we have

$$\zeta = \theta - \xi = \theta + (-\xi) = -\xi.$$

Hence we obtain the following corollary of (3.13).

COROLLARY 3.14. *For any given rational number ξ, we have*

$$\xi - \xi = \xi + (-\xi) = \theta.$$

Now we will identify the integers $\mathcal{Z}$ with a subset of the set Q of rational numbers. For this purpose, we define a function

$$j : \mathcal{Z} \to Q$$

by taking $j(x) = p(1, x)$ for every $x \in \mathcal{Z}$.

PROPOSITION 3.15. *The function $j : \mathcal{Z} \to Q$ is injective. Furthermore, j preserves order, addition, and multiplication; that is, for any two integers a and b, the following three statements are true:*

(i) $a < b$ *implies* $j(a) < j(b)$
(ii) $j(a + b) = j(a) + j(b)$
(iii) $j(ab) = j(a)j(b)$.

Proof. To prove that j is injective, let x and y denote any two integers such that $j(x) = j(y)$. This implies $(1, x) \sim (1, y)$. It follows from the definition of $\sim$ that $x = y$. Hence j is injective.

The verifications of the statements (i), (ii), and (iii) are straightforward and hence omitted.‖

The proposition (3.15) shows us that there is practically no difference between the integers $\mathcal{Z}$ and the members of the subset $j(\mathcal{Z})$ of Q. Because of this, we may identify them; in other words, we may denote the rational number $j(x)$ simply by the integer x itself. This having been done, the set $\mathcal{Z}$ of integers will be considered as a subset of Q and the function $j : \mathcal{Z} \to Q$ becomes the inclusion function.

In particular, the rational number θ is identified with the integer 0 and, hereafter, will be denoted by 0. On the other hand, the integer 1 is identified with the rational number $j(1)$. Thus, as a rational number, 1 is the equivalence class of X defined by

$$1 = \{(a, b) \in X \mid a = b\}.$$

This rational number 1 plays a special role in multiplication, as given by the following proposition.

PROPOSITION 3.16.   *For every rational number ξ, we have $\xi 1 = \xi$.*

Proof.   Let $(a, b) \in \xi$ and consider the pair $(1, 1) \in 1$. By the definition of product, we have

$$\xi 1 = p(a1, b1) = p(a, b) = \xi.$$

This proves (3.16).‖

In order to study division, let us first define the *reciprocal,* or *inverse,* ξ^{-1} of a nonzero rational number ξ. For this purpose, choose a pair $(a, b) \in \xi$. Since $\xi \neq 0$, we have $b \neq 0$. Hence (b, a) is a member of X. Obviously, the rational number $p(b, a)$ does not depend on the choice of the pair (a, b) from the equivalence class ξ. Hence we may define the *reciprocal* of the nonzero rational number ξ to be the rational number

$$\xi^{-1} = p(b, a).$$

Since $a \neq 0$, we have $\xi^{-1} \neq 0$. Then it is obvious that

$$(\xi^{-1})^{-1} = \xi.$$

As a direct consequence of the definition, we also have $1^{-1} = 1$.

To define division, let $\xi \neq 0$ and η denote given rational numbers. Then we define the *quotient η/ξ of η over ξ* by taking

$$\eta/\xi = \eta \xi^{-1}.$$

PROPOSITION 3.17.   *For any two rational numbers $\xi \neq 0$ and η, there exists a unique rational number ζ such that $\xi\zeta = \eta$. Furthermore, we have $\zeta = \eta/\xi$.*

Proof.   Choose $(a, b) \in \xi$ and $(c, d) \in \eta$. Then we have $\xi^{-1} = p(b, a)$ and hence

$$\eta/\xi = \eta\xi^{-1} = p(bc, ad)$$
$$\xi(\eta/\xi) = p(abc, abd) = p(c, d) = \eta.$$

This establishes existence. To prove uniqueness, let ζ denote any rational number satisfying $\xi\zeta = \eta$. Then we have

$$\xi\zeta = \xi(\eta/\xi).$$

Since $\xi \neq 0$, it follows from the cancellation law for multiplication of rational numbers that $\zeta = \eta/\xi$.‖

In particular, if we take $\eta = 1$, then we have

$$\zeta = 1/\xi = 1\xi^{-1} = \xi^{-1}.$$

Hence we obtain the following corollary of (3.17).

COROLLARY 3.18. *For any given nonzero rational number ξ, we have*

$$\xi/\xi = \xi\xi^{-1} = 1.$$

The condition $\xi \neq 0$ in (3.17) is essential. Suppose $\xi = 0$. In case $\eta \neq 0$, no rational number ζ can satisfy $\xi\zeta = \eta$, since $0\zeta = 0 \neq \eta$. In case $\eta = 0$, every rational number ζ satisfies $\xi\zeta = \eta$.

Having imbedded Z as a subset of Q and defined the quotients in Q, we are able to establish the following proposition concerning the natural projection $p: X \to Q$.

PROPOSITION 3.19. *For every member (a, b) of X, we have*

$$p(a, b) = b/a \in Q.$$

Proof. According to the definitions, we have

$$\begin{aligned}
p(a, b) &= p(1, b)p(a, 1) \\
&= p(1, b)[p(1, a)]^{-1} \\
&= j(b)/j(a) \\
&= b/a.
\end{aligned}$$

This proves (3.19).‖

Since the natural projection $j: X \to Q$ is surjective, (3.19) shows that every rational number can be represented as the quotient b/a of an integer b over a nonzero integer a. These quotients of integers are called *fractions*.

Consider a positive rational number ξ. By (3.2), there exists a regular member (a, b) of X with

$$\xi = p(a, b) = b/a.$$

Since (a, b) is regular, we have $a > 0$. Since ξ is positive, it follows from (3.3) that $b > 0$. Hence ξ can be represented as the quotient b/a of two positive integers. The quotients of positive integers are called *positive fractions*. Thus every positive rational number can be represented by a positive fraction.

A positive fraction b/a is said to be *in its lowest terms* if the positive integers a and b are relatively prime.

PROPOSITION 3.20. *Every positive rational number can be uniquely represented by a positive fraction in its lowest terms.*

Proof. Let ξ denote any positive rational number. Then there exist two positive integers a and b with

$$\xi = b/a.$$

Let k denote the greatest common divisor of the positive integers a and b. Then there exist two relatively prime positive integers c and d satisfying $a = kc$ and $b = kd$. According to the definition of $\sim$ in X, we have $(a, b) \sim (c, d)$. This implies

$$\xi = b/a = p(a, b) = p(c, d) = d/c.$$

Hence ξ can be represented by a positive fraction d/c in its lowest terms.

To prove the uniqueness, consider any two positive fractions b/a and d/c in lowest terms with

$$b/a = \xi = d/c.$$

This implies $ad = bc$. Since a and b are relatively prime, it follows that a is a divisor of c. Hence there exists a positive integer e such that $c = ae$. According to the cancellation law, this implies $d = be$. Since c and d are relatively prime, it follows that $e = 1$. Hence we obtain $c = a$ and $d = b$.∥

The proposition (3.20) shows that the positive rational numbers are precisely the positive fractions with lowest terms. On the other hand, the negation function $r:Q \to Q$ sends the positive rational numbers bijectively onto the negative rational numbers, the latter are precisely the negations of the positive fractions with lowest terms.

Hereafter, since we have already constructed the rational numbers and have identified the integers as special rational numbers, it is no longer necessary to use lower case Greek letters to denote rational numbers.

In the system Q of rational numbers, we have seen that the difference $b - a$ is always uniquely defined and that the quotient b/a is uniquely defined iff $a \neq 0$. Hence the system Q appears to be very satisfactory. However, there are still numerous operations which frequently fail to work in Q. One of them is the operation of taking square roots. For example, we have the following proposition.

PROPOSITION 3.21.   *There exists no rational number x satisfying $x^2 = 2$.*

Proof. To prove by the indirect method, assume that x is a rational number satisfying $x^2 = 2$. Since $0^2 = 0$, we have $x \neq 0$. Since $(-x)^2 = x^2$, we may assume $x > 0$. According to (3.20), there exist two relatively prime positive integers a and b such that

$$x = b/a$$

holds. Since $x^2 = 2$, this implies

$$2a^2 = b^2.$$

It follows that 2 is a divisor of b; that is, there exists a positive integer d with

$$b = 2d.$$

Substituting this into $2a^2 = b^2$ and cancelling one factor 2, we obtain

$$a^2 = 2d^2.$$

This implies that 2 is a divisor of a; that is, there exists a positive integer c with

$$a = 2c.$$

It follows that a and b have a common divisor. This contradicts our assumption that a and b are relatively prime.‖

To conclude the present section, let us define the *absolute value* $| x |$ of an arbitrarily given rational number x by setting

$$| x | = \begin{cases} x, & \text{(if } x > 0) \\ 0, & \text{(if } x = 0) \\ -x, & \text{(if } x < 0). \end{cases}$$

Hence $| x | \geqslant 0$ and the following proposition can be easily verified.

PROPOSITION 3.22. *For arbitrarily given rational numbers x and y, the following three statements are true:*

(i) $| -x | = | x |$
(ii) $| xy | = | x | | y |$
(iii) $| (| x | - | y |) | \leqslant | x + y | \leqslant | x | + | y |.$

EXERCISES

3A. Let a, b, c, and d denote arbitrary rational numbers. Prove the equalities and inequalities in Exercises 1A, 1B, and 2A.

3B. Let $a \neq 0$, b, $c \neq 0$, and d denote given rational numbers. Prove the following statements:
   (i) $b/a = d/c$ iff $ad = bc$
   (ii) $(b/a) + (d/c) = (ad + bc)/ac$
   (iii) $(b/a)(d/c) = (bd)/(ac).$

3C. Let p denote any prime positive integer. Prove the following statements:
   (i) There exists no rational number x satisfying $x^2 = p$.
   (ii) There exists no rational number x satisfying $x^3 = p$.

3D. Prove the countability of the set Q of rational numbers by using the definition of Q as a quotient set of $X = (Z \setminus \{0\}) \times Z$.

3E. Consider the Cartesian product $W = (Q \setminus \{0\}) \times Q$ and define a relation $\sim$ in W by setting $(a, b) \sim (c, d)$ iff $ad = bc$. Prove that $\sim$ is an equivalence relation in W and denote the quotient set by $T = W/\sim$. Define a linear order, addition, and multiplication in T precisely as in the text for Q. Consider the function $h: W \to Q$ defined by $h(a, b) = b/a$ for every $(a, b) \in W$. Prove that the inverse images $h^{-1}(x)$, $x \in Q$, are precisely the members of T. Hence h induces a bijective function $k: T \to Q$. Verify that k preserves order, sum, and product. Thus, there is no essential difference between T and Q. This shows that this process, applied on Q as on Z, does not lead to a larger system of numbers.

4. REAL NUMBERS

According to the Pythagorean theorem, the length x of any diagonal of a square with unit sides must satisfy the equation

$$x^2 = 1^2 + 1^2 = 2.$$

Hence there should be a "number" x satisfying $x^2 = 2$. However, by (3.21), there exists no rational number x which satisfies $x^2 = 2$. To escape from this "dilemma of Pythagoras," one has to create *irrational numbers*, that is, numbers which are not quotients of integers. For this purpose, we shall construct a new system R of numbers, called *real numbers*, and identify the rational numbers Q as a part of R.

Among methods of constructing real numbers, those developed by G. Cantor and R. Dedekind are most well known. In Cantor's method, sequences of rational numbers are used to construct the real numbers; while in Dedekind's, the cuts in the rational numbers play the basic role. Here, we shall choose Cantor's method for constructing real numbers because of its similarity to the methods we used to construct integers and rational numbers in the preceding two sections.

By a sequence of rational numbers, we mean a function

$$f: N \to Q$$

from the set N of natural numbers into the set Q of rational numbers. For every $n \in N$, the rational number $f(n)$ is called the nth *term* of the sequence f. Hence the sequence f is usually denoted by

$$f(1), f(2), \ldots, f(n), \ldots.$$

A sequence $f : N \to Q$ of rational numbers is said to be *fundamental* iff, for every positive rational number d, there exists a natural number k (depending on d) such that

$$| f(m) - f(n) | < d$$

holds for every pair of natural numbers m and n satisfying $m > k$ and $n > k$. Note that the preceding inequality is equivalent to the following:

$$-d < f(m) - f(n) < d.$$

Fundamental sequences are sometimes called *Cauchy sequences.*

Consider the set F of all fundamental sequences of rational numbers. Define a relation $\sim$ in the set F as follows. For any two fundamental sequences $f, g : N \to Q$, we define

$$f \sim g$$

iff, for any positive rational number d, there exists a natural number k (depending on d) such that

$$| f(n) - g(n) | < d$$

holds for every natural number $n > k$.

LEMMA 4.1.   *The relation $\sim$ in F is an equivalence relation.*

Proof.   We have to verify that $\sim$ is reflexive, symmetric, and transitive.

To prove that $\sim$ is reflexive, let f denote any member of F and let d be any given positive rational number. Since

$$| f(n) - f(n) | = 0 < d$$

holds for every $n \in N$, we have $f \sim f$. Hence $\sim$ is reflexive.

To prove that $\sim$ is symmetric, let f and g denote any two members of F such that $f \sim g$ holds. Let d be any given positive rational number. Since $f \sim g$, there exists a natural number k such that $| f(n) - g(n) | < d$ holds for every $n > k$. Because of

$$| g(n) - f(n) | = | f(n) - g(n) |$$

it follows that $| g(n) - f(n) | < d$ holds for every $n > k$. This implies $g \sim f$. Hence $\sim$ is symmetric.

To prove that $\sim$ is transitive, let f, g, and h denote any three members of F such that $f \sim g$ and $g \sim h$ hold. Let d denote any given positive rational number. Since $f \sim g$, there exists a natural number i such that

$$| f(n) - g(n) | < \tfrac{1}{2}d$$

holds for every natural number $n > i$. Similarly, since $g \sim h$, there exists a natural number j such that

$$| g(n) - h(n) | < \tfrac{1}{2}d$$

holds for every natural number $n > j$. Now let

$$k = \max (i, j);$$

in words, k denotes the larger of the two natural numbers i and j. Since

$$f(n) - h(n) = [f(n) - g(n)] + [g(n) - h(n)]$$

holds for all $n \, \epsilon \, \mathcal{N}$, it follows from (3.22) that

$$| f(n) - h(n) | \leqslant | f(n) - g(n) | + | g(n) - h(n) |$$
$$< \tfrac{1}{2}d + \tfrac{1}{2}d = d$$

holds for every natural number $n > k$. This proves $f \sim h$. Hence $\sim$ is transitive.$\|$

According to (I, §8), this equivalence relation $\sim$ in F defines a quotient set of F which will be denoted by

$$R = F/\sim.$$

The members of R will be called *real numbers*. Thus the real numbers are the equivalence classes in F with respect to $\sim$.

Next, we shall define a relation $<$ in the set R of real numbers. For this purpose, let ξ and η denote any two given real numbers. Select arbitrary members $f \, \epsilon \, \xi$ and $g \, \epsilon \, \eta$. We define

$$\xi < \eta$$

iff there exists a positive rational number d together with a natural number k such that

$$g(n) - f(n) > d$$

holds for every natural number $n > k$.

To justify our definition of $\xi < \eta$, we have to verify that it does not depend on the choice of the members f and g from the equivalence classes ξ and η. For this purpose, let $f' \, \epsilon \, \xi$ and $g' \, \epsilon \, \eta$ be arbitrarily given. Assume that $f \, \epsilon \, \xi$ and $g \, \epsilon \, \eta$ satisfy the condition in the preceding definition. Since $f \sim f'$, there exists a natural number i such that

$$| f(n) - f'(n) | < \tfrac{1}{4}d$$

holds for every natural number $n > i$. Similarly, since $g' \sim g$, there exists a natural number j such that

$$| g'(n) - g(n) | < \tfrac{1}{4}d$$

holds for every natural number $n > j$. Let

$$h = \max \ (i, j, k);$$

that is, h denotes the largest of the three natural numbers i, j, and k. Since

$$g'(n) - f'(n) = [g(n) - f(n)] + [f(n) - f'(n)] + [g'(n) - g(n)]$$

holds for every $n \in \mathcal{N}$, it follows that

$$
\begin{aligned}
g'(n) - f'(n) &\geqslant g(n) - f(n) - | f(n) - f'(n) | - | g'(n) - g(n) | \\
&> d - \tfrac{1}{4}d - \tfrac{1}{4}d = \tfrac{1}{2}d
\end{aligned}
$$

holds for every natural number $n > h$. This completes the justification of our definition.

PROPOSITION 4.2. *For any two real numbers ξ and η, one and only one of the following three statements is true:*

(i) $\xi < \eta$,   (ii) $\xi = \eta$,   (iii) $\xi > \eta$.

Proof. It is obvious that no two of the three statements (i)–(iii) can be true simultaneously. Hence it suffices to prove that $\xi = \eta$ holds whenever $\xi < \eta$ and $\xi > \eta$ are both false.

For this purpose, let $f \epsilon \xi$ and $g \epsilon \eta$. Let d denote any given positive rational number. According to the definition of fundamental sequences, there exists a natural number k such that

$$| f(m) - f(n) | < \tfrac{1}{3}d, \qquad | g(m) - g(n) | < \tfrac{1}{3}d$$

hold for every $m > k$ and every $n > k$.

Since $\eta < \xi$ is false, there exists a natural number $m > k$ such that

$$f(m) - g(m) \leqslant \tfrac{1}{3}d$$

holds. Hence we have

$$
\begin{aligned}
f(n) - g(n) &= [f(n) - f(m)] + [f(m) - g(m)] + [g(m) - g(n)] \\
&\leqslant | f(n) - f(m) | + [f(m) - g(m)] + | g(m) - g(n) | \\
&< \tfrac{1}{3}d + \tfrac{1}{3}d + \tfrac{1}{3}d = d
\end{aligned}
$$

for every $n > k$. Similarly, since $\xi < \eta$ is false, we have

$$g(n) - f(n) < d$$

for every $n > k$. Multiplying both sides by -1, we obtain

$$f(n) - g(n) = -[g(n) - f(n)] > -d$$

for every $n > k$. Hence

$$| f(n) - g(n) | < d$$

holds for every $n > k$. This implies $f \sim g$ and hence $\xi = \eta.\|$

PROPOSITION 4.3.   *The relation $<$ in the set R of real numbers is a linear order.*

Proof.   To prove the transitivity of the relation $<$ in R, let ξ, η, ζ denote arbitrary real numbers satisfying $\xi < \eta$ and $\eta < \zeta$. Select fundamental sequences $f \epsilon \xi$, $g \epsilon \eta$, and $h \epsilon \zeta$. Since $\xi < \eta$, there exists a positive rational number b together with a natural number i such that

$$g(n) - f(n) > b$$

holds for every natural number $n > i$. Similarly, since $n < \zeta$, there exists a positive rational number c together with a natural number j such that

$$h(n) - g(n) > c$$

holds for every natural number $n > j$.

Let $d = b + c$ and $k = \max (i, j)$. Then we have

$$h(n) - f(n) = [g(n) - f(n)] + [h(n) - g(n)] > b + c = d$$

for every natural number $n > k$. This implies $\xi < \zeta$. Thus we have proved the transitivity of the relation $<$ in R. Hence $<$ is a partial order.

Because of (4.2), the conditions (**L1**) and (**L2**) in (I, §8) are satisfied by this partial order $<$ in R. Hence $<$ is a linear order. $\|$

Let $z : N \to Q$ denote the member of F defined by $z(n) = 0$ for every $n \epsilon N$. The real number which contains this member z of F is called the *real number zero* and will be denoted by θ until otherwise stated.

A real number ξ is said to be *positive* iff $\theta < \xi$ holds; ξ is said to be *negative* iff $\xi < \theta$ holds. The following corollary is an immediate consequence of (4.2).

COROLLARY 4.4.   *For any real number $\xi \epsilon R$, one and only one of the following three statements is true:*

(**i**)   *ξ is positive*
(**ii**)   *ξ is the real number zero*
(**iii**)   *ξ is negative.*

For convenience of further study in the remainder of this section, we shall let

$$p : F \to R$$

denote the *natural projection* of F onto its quotient set R. As defined in (I, §8), p is a surjective function sending each fundamental sequence $f \in F$ to the equivalence class $p(f) \in R$ which contains f.

On the other hand, the following lemma will be found useful.

LEMMA 4.5. *Every fundamental sequence* $f : N \to Q$ *of rational numbers is bounded; that is, there exists a positive rational number u such that* $| f(n) | \leqslant u$ *holds for every* $n \in N$.

Proof. Let $f : N \to Q$ be any fundamental sequence of rational numbers. Then there exists a natural number k such that

$$| f(m) - f(n) | < 1$$

holds for every $m > k$ and every $n > k$. Let u denote the largest of the $k + 1$ rational numbers

$$| f(1) |, | f(2) |, \ldots, | f(k) |, | f(k + 1) | + 1.$$

It suffices to prove that

$$| f(n) | \leqslant u$$

holds for every $n \in N$. This is obvious for $n \leqslant k$. Assume $n > k$. Then we have

$$\begin{aligned} | f(n) | &= | f(k + 1) + [f(n) - f(k + 1)] | \\ &\leqslant | f(k + 1) | + | f(n) - f(k + 1) | \\ &< | f(k + 1) | + 1 \leqslant u. \end{aligned}$$

This completes the proof of (4.5).‖

Let $f, g : N \to Q$ denote any two given sequences of rational numbers. Then we can define two sequences

$$f + g : N \to Q, \qquad fg : N \to Q$$

of rational numbers by taking

$$(f + g)(n) = f(n) + g(n)$$
$$(fg)(n) = f(n)g(n)$$

for every $n \in N$. The sequences $f + g$ and fg are called the *sum* and the *product* of the given sequences f and g, respectively.

PROPOSITION 4.6. *If the given sequences* $f, g : N \to Q$ *are fundamental, then so are* $f + g$ *and* fg.

Proof. To prove that $f + g$ is fundamental, let d denote any given positive rational number. Since f is fundamental, there exists a natural number i such that

$$| f(m) - f(n) | < \tfrac{1}{2} d$$

holds for every $m > i$ and every $n > i$. Similarly, since g is fundamental, there exists a natural number j such that

$$| g(m) - g(n) | < \tfrac{1}{2}d$$

holds for every $m > j$ and every $n > j$.

Let $k = \max (i, j)$. Then we have

$$
\begin{aligned}
| (f + g)(m) - (f + g)(n) | &= | f(m) - f(n) + g(m) - g(n) | \\
&\leqslant | f(m) - f(n) | + | g(m) - g(n) | \\
&< \tfrac{1}{2}d + \tfrac{1}{2}d = d
\end{aligned}
$$

for every $m > k$ and every $n > k$. This proves that $f + g$ is fundamental.

To prove that fg is fundamental, let d denote any given positive rational number. Since f and g are fundamental, it follows from (4.5) that there exist positive rational numbers u and v such that $| f(n) | \leqslant u$ and $| g(n) | \leqslant v$ hold for every $n \epsilon N$. Since f is fundamental and $d/2v$ is a positive rational number, there exists a natural number i such that

$$| f(m) - f(n) | < \frac{d}{2v}$$

holds for every $m > i$ and every $n > i$. Similarly, there exists a natural number j such that

$$| g(m) - g(n) | < \frac{d}{2u}$$

holds for every $m > j$ and every $n > j$.

Let $k = \max (i, j)$. Then we have

$$
\begin{aligned}
| (fg)(m) - (fg)(n) | &= | f(m)g(m) - f(n)g(n) | \\
&= | f(m)[g(m) - g(n)] + g(n)[f(m) - f(n)] | \\
&\leqslant | f(m) | | g(m) - g(n) | + | g(n) | | f(m) - f(n) | \\
&< u\left(\frac{d}{2u}\right) + v\left(\frac{d}{2v}\right) = \frac{d}{2} + \frac{d}{2} = d
\end{aligned}
$$

for every $m > k$ and every $n > k$. This proves that fg is fundamental. $\|$

To define addition and multiplication of real numbers, let ξ and η denote any two given real numbers. By definition, ξ and η are equivalence classes in F with respect to $\sim$. Choose fundamental sequences $f \epsilon \xi$ and $g \epsilon \eta$. According to (4.6), the sequences $f + g$ and fg are also fundamental. It is straightforward to verify that the real numbers $p(f + g)$ and $p(fg)$ do not depend on the choice of the sequences f and g from the given equivalence classes ξ and η. Hence we may define the *sum* $\xi + \eta$ and the *product* $\xi\eta$ by taking

$$\xi + \eta = p(f + g), \qquad \xi\eta = p(fg).$$

Having defined addition and multiplication as above, one can easily verify the following theorem.

THEOREM 4.7. *Let α, β, γ, and δ denote arbitrarily given real numbers. Then we have the laws* (1)–(5) *in* (2.9) *with* 0 *replaced by* θ.

The real number θ plays a special role in addition and multiplication as given by the following proposition, which is obvious from the definitions.

PROPOSITION 4.8. *For every real number ξ, we have $\xi + \theta = \xi$ and $\xi\theta = \theta$.*

In order to study subtraction, let us first define the *negation*, $-\xi$, of any given real number ξ. For this purpose, consider a fundamental sequence $f \in \xi$. Obviously, the sequence

$$-f : \mathcal{N} \to Q$$

defined by $(-f)(n) = - [f(n)]$ for every $n \in \mathcal{N}$ is fundamental, and the real number $p(-f)$ does not depend on the choice of f from the equivalence class ξ. Hence we may define the *negation* of the real number ξ to be the real number

$$-\xi = p(-f).$$

The following proposition can be easily verified.

PROPOSITION 4.9. *For arbitrary real numbers ξ and η, we have the statements* (i)–(vi) *in* (2.11) *with* 0 *replaced by* θ.

By the *negation function* of R, we mean the function

$$r : R \to R$$

defined by $r(\xi) = -\xi$ for every $\xi \in R$. One can easily verify that the composition $r \circ r$ is the identity function on R. Hence it follows from (I, 6.4) that r is bijective and is its own inverse. By (ii)–(iv) of (4.9), r sends the positive real numbers bijectively onto the negative real numbers, and vice versa.

To define subtraction, let ξ and η denote arbitrarily given real numbers. Then we define their *difference* $\eta - \xi$ by taking

$$\eta - \xi = \eta + (-\xi).$$

The following proposition can be easily verified.

PROPOSITION 4.10. *For any two real numbers ξ and η, there exists a unique real number ζ such that $\xi + \zeta = \eta$ holds. Furthermore, we have $\zeta = \eta - \xi$.*

In particular, if we take $\eta = \theta$, then we have

$$\zeta = \theta - \xi = \theta + (-\xi) = -\xi.$$

Hence we obtain the following corollary of (4.10).

COROLLARY 4.11. *For any given real number ξ, we have*

$$\xi - \xi = \xi + (-\xi) = \theta.$$

Now we will identify the rational numbers Q with a subset of the set R of real numbers. For this purpose, we define a function

$$j:Q \to R$$

as follows. For each $x \in Q$, the *constant sequence*

$$f_x:N \to Q$$

given by $f_x(n) = x$ for every $n \in N$ is clearly fundamental. Hence we may define j by taking $j(x) = p(f_x)$ for every $x \in Q$.

The following proposition can be easily verified.

PROPOSITION 4.12. *The function $j:Q \to R$ is injective. Furthermore, j preserves order, addition, and multiplication; that is, for any two rational numbers a and b, the following three statements are true:*

(i) $a < b$ implies $j(a) < j(b)$
(ii) $j(a + b) = j(a) + j(b)$
(iii) $j(ab) = j(a)j(b)$.

The proposition (4.12) shows us that there is practically no difference between the rational numbers Q and the members of the subset $j(Q)$ of R. Because of this, we may identify them; in other words, we may denote the real number $j(x)$ simply by the rational number x itself. This having been done, the set Q of rational numbers will be considered as a subset of R and the function $j:Q \to R$ becomes the inclusion function.

In particular, the real number θ is identified with the rational number 0 and, hereafter, will be denoted by 0. On the other hand, the rational number 1 is identified with the real number $j(1)$. This real number 1 plays a special role in multiplication, as given by the following proposition which is obvious from the definition.

PROPOSITION 4.13. *For every real number ξ, we have $\xi 1 = \xi$.*

The real numbers in $R \setminus Q$ are called *irrational numbers.*

In order to study division, let us first define the *reciprocal*, or *inverse*, ξ^{-1} of a nonzero real number ξ. For this purpose, choose a fundamental sequence $f \in \xi$. Since $\xi \neq 0$, it follows from the definition of the order $<$ in R that there exists a positive rational number d together with a natural number k such that

$$| f(n) | > d$$

holds for every natural number $n > k$. Thus we may define a sequence $g : \mathcal{N} \to Q$ by taking

$$g(n) = 1/f(n + k)$$

for every $n \in \mathcal{N}$. One can easily verify that g is fundamental and that the real number $p(g)$ depends only on the given real number ξ. Hence we may define the *reciprocal* of the nonzero real number ξ to be the real number

$$\xi^{-1} = p(g).$$

Since f is bounded according to (4.5), one can easily prove that $\xi^{-1} \neq 0$. Then it is obvious that

$$(\xi^{-1})^{-1} = \xi.$$

As a direct consequence of the definition, we also have $1^{-1} = 1$.

To define division, let $\xi \neq 0$ and η denote given real numbers. Then we define the *quotient* η/ξ of η over ξ by taking

$$\eta/\xi = \eta\xi^{-1}.$$

The following proposition can be easily verified.

PROPOSITION 4.14. *For any two real numbers $\xi \neq 0$ and η, there exists a unique real number ζ such that $\xi\zeta = \eta$ holds. Furthermore, we have $\zeta = \eta/\xi$.*

In particular, if we take $\eta = 1$, then we have

$$\zeta = 1/\xi = 1\xi^{-1} = \xi^{-1}.$$

Hence we obtain the following corollary of (4.14).

COROLLARY 4.15. *For any given nonzero real number ξ, we have*

$$\xi/\xi = \xi\xi^{-1} = 1.$$

The condition $\xi \neq 0$ in (4.14) is essential. Suppose $\xi = 0$. In case $\eta \neq 0$, no real number ζ can satisfy $\xi\zeta = \eta$ since $0\zeta = 0 \neq \eta$. In case $\eta = 0$, every real number ζ satisfies $\xi\zeta = \eta$.

For an example of irrational numbers, let us consider the square roots of 2. The arithmetic process of finding the decimals of the positive square root of 2 defines a sequence

$$f : \mathcal{N} \to Q$$

of rational numbers; namely, we have

$$f(1) = 1, \quad f(2) = 1.4, \quad f(3) = 1.41, \quad f(4) = 1.414, \quad \ldots .$$

One can easily verify that f is fundamental and hence determines a real number $p(f)$. This real number $p(f)$ will be denoted by $\sqrt{2}$. It is straightforward to verify that

$$(\sqrt{2})^2 = 2$$

holds. In view of (3.21), this implies that $\sqrt{2}$ is an irrational number.

The subset Q of R has an important property given by the following theorem.

THEOREM 4.16. *The subset Q of rational numbers is dense in the set R of real numbers; that is, for any two real numbers ξ and η with $\xi < \eta$, there exists a rational number r such that $\xi < r < \eta$ holds.*

Proof. Choose fundamental sequences $f \epsilon \xi$ and $g \epsilon \eta$. Since $\xi < \eta$ holds, there exists a positive rational number d together with a natural number k such that

$$g(n) - f(n) > d$$

holds for every natural number $n > k$. Since f is fundamental, there exists a natural number i such that

$$| f(m) - f(n) | < \tfrac{1}{3}d$$

holds for every $m > i$ and every $n > i$. Similarly, since g is fundamental, there exists a natural number j such that

$$| g(m) - g(n) | < \tfrac{1}{3}d$$

holds for every $m > j$ and every $n > j$.

Let $h = \max (i, j, k)$. Consider the rational number

$$r = \tfrac{1}{2}[f(h + 1) + g(h + 1)].$$

It remains to prove $\xi < r < \eta$. For this purpose, we have

$$
\begin{aligned}
r - f(n) &= \tfrac{1}{2}[f(h + 1) + g(h + 1)] - f(n) \\
&= \tfrac{1}{2}[g(h + 1) - f(h + 1)] + [f(h + 1) - f(n)] \\
&> \tfrac{1}{2}d - \tfrac{1}{3}d = \tfrac{1}{6}d, \\
g(n) - r &= g(n) - \tfrac{1}{2}[f(h + 1) + g(h + 1)] \\
&= \tfrac{1}{2}[g(h + 1) - f(h + 1)] + [g(n) - g(h + 1)] \\
&> \tfrac{1}{2}d - \tfrac{1}{3}d = \tfrac{1}{6}d
\end{aligned}
$$

for every $n > h$. This implies $\xi < r < \eta.\|$

Hereafter, since we have already constructed the real numbers and have identified the rational numbers as special real numbers, it is no longer necessary to use lower case Greek letters to denote real numbers.

To conclude the present section, let us define the *absolute value* $|x|$ of an arbitrary real number x by setting

$$|x| = \begin{cases} x & (\text{if } x > 0), \\ 0 & (\text{if } x = 0), \\ -x & (\text{if } x < 0). \end{cases}$$

Hence $|x| \geqslant 0$ and the following proposition can be easily verified.

PROPOSITION 4.17. *For arbitrarily given real numbers x and y, the following three statements are true:*

(i) $|-x| = |x|$

(ii) $|xy| = |x||y|$

(iii) $|(|x| - |y|)| \leqslant |x+y| \leqslant |x| + |y|$.

EXERCISES

4A. Let a, b, c, and d denote arbitrary real numbers. Prove the equalities and inequalities in Exercises 1A, 1B, and 2A.

4B. By means of the countability argument, prove that the irrational numbers are dense in the system R of real numbers; that is, for any two real numbers a and b with $a < b$, there exists an irrational number x such that $a < x < b$ holds.

4C. Let r denote a rational number and x an irrational number. Prove that $r + x$ and rx are irrational numbers.

4D. Let x and y denote any two positive real numbers. Prove that there exists a natural number n satisfying $na > b$.

4E. A real number x is said to be *algebraic* iff it satisfies an equation

$$a_0 x^n + a_1 x^{n-1} + \cdots + a_{n-1} x + a_n = 0$$

with rational coefficients $a_0 \neq 0$, $a_1, \ldots, a_n$; otherwise, x is said to be *transcendental*. By the countability of the set of these equations, prove that the set A of all algebraic real numbers is countable. Hence the set T of all transcendental real numbers is not countable. For examples of transcendental numbers, we have

$$e = 2.71828 \cdots, \qquad \pi = 3.14159 \cdots.$$

4F. By a *sequence of real numbers*, we mean a function $\phi : N \to R$. The function ϕ is said to be *fundamental* iff, for every positive real number δ, there exists a natural number k such that

$$|\phi(m) - \phi(n)| < \delta$$

holds for every $m > k$ and every $n > k$. Prove that the system R of real numbers is *complete;* that is, for any given fundamental sequence $\phi:\mathcal{N} \to R$, there exists a real number ξ having the property that, for every positive real number δ, there exists a natural number k such that

$$| \phi(n) - \xi | < \delta$$

holds for every natural number $n > k$. Then show that Cantor's method, applied on R as on Q, does not lead to a larger system of numbers.

5. COMPLEX NUMBERS

As a consequence of (4.7) and (4.9), the square x^2 of any real number x is nonnegative; that is, $x^2 \geqslant 0$. Hence, a simple algebraic equation such as

$$x^2 + 1 = 0$$

has no solution in the system R of real numbers. In order to make these equations solvable, one has to create *imaginary numbers.* By forming a Cartesian product, we shall construct a new system C of numbers, called *complex numbers,* and identify the real numbers R as a part of C.

For this purpose, let us consider the Cartesian square

$$C = R^2 = R \times R$$

of the system R of real numbers. The members of C are ordered pairs (x, y) of real numbers and will be called *complex numbers.*

To define addition and multiplication of complex numbers, let $\xi = (a, b)$ and $\eta = (c, d)$ denote any two given complex numbers. We define the *sum* $\xi + \eta$ and the *product* $\xi\eta$ by taking

$$\xi + \eta = (a + c, b + d)$$
$$\xi\eta = (ac - bd, ad + bc).$$

To identify the real numbers R as a subset of the set C of complex numbers, let us define a function

$$j:R \to C$$

by taking $j(x) = (x, 0)$ for every $x \in R$.

PROPOSITION 5.1.   *The function $j:R \to C$ is injective. Furthermore, j preserves addition and multiplication; that is, for any two real numbers a and b, the following two statements are true:*

(i) $j(a + b) = j(a) + j(b)$
(ii) $j(ab) = j(a)j(b)$.

Proof. To prove that j is injective, let us consider the natural projection

$$p:C \to R$$

defined by $p(x, y) = x$ for every $(x, y) \in C$. Then the composition $p \circ j$ is clearly the identity function on R. According to (I, 6.3), this implies that j is injective.

The equalities (**i**) and (**ii**) can be verified as follows:

$$j(a + b) = (a + b, 0) = (a, 0) + (b, 0) = j(a) + j(b)$$
$$j(ab) = (ab, 0) = (a, 0)(b, 0) = j(a)j(b).$$

This completes the proof of (5.1).‖

Because of (5.1), we may identify R with the subset $j(R)$ of C; in other words, we may denote the complex number $j(x) = (x, 0)$ simply by the real number x itself. This having been done, the set R of real numbers will be considered as a subset of the set C of complex numbers and the function $j:R \to C$ becomes the inclusion function. In geometric language, the set C of complex numbers is called the *complex plane* and its subset R of real numbers is called its *real axis*.

In particular, the real number 0 is identified with the complex number $(0, 0)$ and the real number 1 is identified with the complex number $(1, 0)$. These two complex numbers 0 and 1 play special roles in addition and multiplication as given in the following proposition which is obvious from the definitions.

PROPOSITION 5.2. *For every complex number ξ, we have*

$$\xi + 0 = \xi, \qquad \xi 0 = 0, \qquad \xi 1 = \xi.$$

The following theorem can be easily verified.

THEOREM 5.3. *Let α, β, γ, and δ denote arbitrarily given complex numbers. Then we have the laws* (1)–(4) *in* (2.9).

In order to study subtraction, let us first define the *negation* $-\xi$ of any given complex number $\xi = (a, b)$ by taking

$$-\xi = (-a, -b).$$

Then the following proposition can be easily verified.

PROPOSITION 5.4. *For arbitrary complex numbers ξ and η, we have the statements* (**i**), (**ii**), (**v**), *and* (**vi**) *in* (2.11).

To define subtraction, let ξ and η denote arbitrarily given complex numbers. Then we define their *difference* $\eta - \xi$ by taking

$$\eta - \xi = \eta + (-\xi).$$

If $\xi = (a, b)$ and $\eta = (c, d)$, then we have

$$\eta - \xi = (c - a, d - b).$$

The following proposition can be easily verified.

PROPOSITION 5.5. *For any two complex numbers ξ and η, there exists a unique complex number ζ such that $\xi + \zeta = \eta$ holds. Furthermore, we have $\zeta = \eta - \xi$.*

In particular, if we take $\eta = 0$, then we have

$$\zeta = 0 - \xi = 0 + (-\xi) = -\xi.$$

Hence we obtain the following corollary of (5.5).

COROLLARY 5.6. *For any given complex number ξ, we have*

$$\xi - \xi = \xi + (-\xi) = 0.$$

In order to study division, let us first define the *reciprocal*, or *inverse*, ξ^{-1} of a nonzero complex number

$$\xi = (a, b) \neq 0.$$

Since $\xi \neq 0$, we have $a^2 + b^2 > 0$. Thus we may define the reciprocal ξ^{-1} of ξ by taking

$$\xi^{-1} = \left(\frac{a}{a^2 + b^2}, \frac{-b}{a^2 + b^2} \right).$$

To define division, let $\xi \neq 0$ and η denote given complex numbers. Then we define the *quotient* η/ξ of η over ξ by taking

$$\eta/\xi = \eta \xi^{-1}.$$

If $\xi = (a, b)$ and $\eta = (c, d)$, then we have

$$\eta/\xi = \left(\frac{ac + bd}{a^2 + b^2}, \frac{ad - bc}{a^2 + b^2} \right).$$

The following proposition can be easily verified.

PROPOSITION 5.7. *For any two complex numbers $\xi \neq 0$ and η, there exists a unique complex number ζ such that $\xi \zeta = \eta$ holds. Furthermore, we have $\zeta = \eta/\xi$.*

In particular, if we take $\eta = 1$, then we have

$$\zeta = 1/\xi = 1\xi^{-1} = \xi^{-1}.$$

Hence we obtain the following corollary of (5.7).

COROLLARY 5.8. *For any given nonzero complex number ξ, we have*

$$\xi/\xi = \xi \xi^{-1} = 1, \qquad (\xi^{-1})^{-1} = \xi.$$

The condition $\xi \neq 0$ in (5.7) is essential. Suppose that $\xi = 0$. In case $\eta \neq 0$, no complex number ζ can satisfy $\xi\zeta = \eta$ since $0\zeta = 0 \neq \eta$. In case $\eta = 0$, every complex number ζ satisfies $\xi\zeta = \eta$.

Hereafter, since we have already constructed the complex numbers and have identified the real numbers as special complex numbers, it is no longer necessary to use lower case Greek letters to denote complex numbers.

The complex numbers in $C \setminus R$ are called *imaginary numbers*. Thus a complex number $z = (x, y)$ is imaginary iff $y \neq 0$. By a *pure imaginary number*, we mean an imaginary number $z = (x, y)$ with $x = 0$. As an example of pure imaginary numbers, we have the *imaginary unit*

$$i = (0, 1).$$

By the definition of the multiplication, one can easily verify that

$$i^2 + 1 = 0.$$

Hence $x = i$ is a solution of the equation $x^2 + 1 = 0$ at the beginning of this section.

For any complex number $z = (x, y)$, the real number x is called the *real part* of z, whereas y is said to be the *imaginary part* of z. In symbols, we have

$$\text{Re}(z) = x, \qquad \text{Im}(z) = y.$$

Thus, we get

$$z = (x, y) = (x, 0) + (0, y) = (x, 0) + (0, 1)(y, 0)$$
$$= x + iy = \text{Re}(z) + i\text{Im}(z).$$

It will be convenient to denote a complex number (x, y) as $x + iy$. In fact, the *rational operations*, namely, addition, subtraction, multiplication, and division, on complex numbers can be performed algebraically on these linear expressions of i followed by replacing i^2 with -1. For example, we have

$$(a + ib) + (c + id) = (a + c) + i(b + d),$$
$$(a + ib) - (c + id) = (a - c) + i(b - d),$$
$$(a + ib)(c + id) = ac + i^2bd + i(ad + bc)$$
$$= (ac - bd) + i(ad + bc),$$
$$\frac{c + id}{a + ib} = \frac{(c + id)(a - ib)}{(a + ib)(a - ib)} = \frac{(ac + bd) + i(ad - bc)}{a^2 + b^2}$$
$$= \frac{ac + bd}{a^2 + b^2} + i\,\frac{ad - bc}{a^2 + b^2}.$$

In the last formula, we have used the *complex conjugate* $a - ib$ of the denominator $a + ib$. In general, we define the *complex conjugate* of an arbitrary complex number $z = x + iy$ to be the complex number

$$\bar{z} = x - iy = \mathrm{Re}(z) - i\mathrm{Im}(z).$$

The following proposition is obvious.

PROPOSITION 5.9. *For arbitrary complex numbers z_1, z_2, and z, we have*

$$\bar{\bar{z}} = z, \quad \overline{z_1 + z_2} = \bar{z}_1 + \bar{z}_2, \quad \overline{z_1 z_2} = \bar{z}_1 \bar{z}_2, \quad \overline{z^{-1}} = \bar{z}^{-1}.$$

By definition, the complex numbers $z = x + iy$ are precisely the points (x, y) of the Euclidean plane in analytic geometry. This is why the set C of all complex numbers is called the *complex plane*. In this geometric representation of the complex numbers, the *origin* is the complex number 0. The x-axis is the *real axis* which consists of all real numbers. The y-axis consists of 0 and all pure imaginary numbers, and it will be referred to as the *imaginary axis*. Then it is obvious that the complex conjugate $\bar{z}$ of any complex number z is the mirror image of z in the real axis of the complex plane.

Next, let us introduce polar coordinates (r, θ) in the complex plane C via

$$x = r \cos \theta, \qquad y = r \sin \theta,$$

with $r \geqslant 0$ and $0 \leqslant \theta < 2\pi$. Then we can write

$$z = x + iy = r(\cos \theta + i \sin \theta).$$

Here, r, called the *magnitude* of z and denoted by $|z|$, is the distance from the origin 0 to the point z determined by

$$r = |z| = \mathcal{J}(x^2 + y^2),$$

whereas θ, called the *amplitude* of z, is the angle between the real axis and the directed line $0z$ and is determined by

$$\tan \theta = y/x.$$

The following proposition can be easily verified.

PROPOSITION 5.10. *For arbitrarily given complex numbers z_1, z_2, and z, the following statements are true:*

(i) $|z| \geqslant 0$
(ii) $|z| = 0$ iff $z = 0$
(iii) $|-z| = |z|$
(iv) $|\bar{z}| = |z|$

(**v**) $|z_1 z_2| = |z_1| |z_2|$

(**vi**) $|(|z_1| - |z_2|)| \leqslant |z_1 + z_2| \leqslant |z_1| + |z_2|$

(**vii**)   *The magnitude of a real number is equal to its absolute value.*

(**viii**)   *The magnitude* $|z_1 - z_2|$ *is equal to the distance between the two points* z_1 *and* z_2 *in the complex plane* C.

EXERCISES

5A. Reduce the following complex numbers to the form $x + iy$ with real x and y:

    (i) $(3 + i) + (-7 + 2i)$

    (ii) $(5 - i) - (-2 - 3i)$

    (iii) $(2 + 3i)(3 - 2i)$

    (iv) $(1 + i)/(1 - i)$

    (v) $(1 + i)^3$

    (vi) $(2 - i)^{-2}$.

5B. Let z denote an arbitrary complex number. Prove the following statements:

    (i) $z + \bar{z} = 2\mathrm{Re}(z)$

    (ii) $z - \bar{z} = 2i\mathrm{Im}(z)$

    (iii) $|\mathrm{Re}(z)| \leqslant |z|$

    (iv) $|\mathrm{Im}(z)| \leqslant |z|$

    (v) $|z| \leqslant |\mathrm{Re}(z)| + |\mathrm{Im}(z)|$.

5C. By mathematical induction, prove that

$$[r(\cos \theta + i \sin \theta)]^n = r^n(\cos n\theta + i \sin n\theta)$$

holds for every natural number n.

5D. Let n denote a given natural number. Find all complex numbers z satisfying $z^n = 1$. These complex numbers are known as the *nth roots of unity*.

5E. Find a complex number z which satisfies the equation

$$(1 + i)z + 3i\bar{z} = 2 + i.$$

5F. Find a complex number z and a complex number w which satisfy the following two equations:

$$i\bar{z} + (1 + i)w = 3 + i,$$
$$(1 + i)z - (6 + i)\bar{w} = 4.$$

Chapter III: ALGEBRAIC STRUCTURES

In the present chapter, we will introduce the various algebraic structures, such as semigroups, groups, rings, integral domains, fields, modules, vector spaces, and algebras, together with some of their elementary properties. Interested readers will be able to study the author's book *Elements of Modern Algebra* for further information.

1. BINARY OPERATIONS

In each of the number systems constructed in Chapter II, we have two binary operations, namely, addition and multiplication.

In general, let X denote an arbitrarily given set and consider the Cartesian square

$$X^2 = X \times X$$

of the set X as defined in (I, §7). We recall that the members of X^2 are the ordered pairs (a, b) of members $a \in X$ and $b \in X$.

By a *binary operation* in the set X, we mean any function

$$\mu : X^2 \to X$$

from X^2 into X itself. In other words, a binary operation μ in a set X assigns to each ordered pair (a, b) of members of the given set X a member $\mu(a, b)$ of X. This member $\mu(a, b)$ will be called the *composite* of a and b.

. EXAMPLES OF BINARY OPERATIONS

(**1**) *Usual addition.* Let X denote any of the number systems constructed in Chapter II. Then a binary operation μ is defined in X by setting

$$\mu(a, b) = a + b$$

for each ordered pair of numbers a and b in the system X. This binary operation μ will be referred to as the *usual addition* in X.

(2) *Usual multiplication.* Let X be the same set as in **(1)**. Then a binary operation μ is defined in X by setting

$$\mu(a, b) = ab$$

for each ordered pair of numbers a and b in the system X. This binary operation μ will be referred to as the *usual multiplication* in X.

(3) *Usual subtraction.* Let X stand for any of the number systems Z, Q, R, and C of Chapter II. Then we can define a binary operation μ in X by taking

$$\mu(a, b) = a - b$$

for each ordered pair of numbers a and b in the system X. This binary operation μ will be referred to as the *usual subtraction* in X.

(4) *Usual composition.* Let S denote an arbitrarily given set and let X stand for the set of all functions

$$f\!:\!S \to S$$

from the set S into itself. Then we can define a binary operation μ in X by taking

$$\mu(f, g) = f \circ g$$

for each ordered pair of members f and g in X. Here, $f \circ g$ denotes the composition of the two functions

$$S \xrightarrow{\;g\;} S \xrightarrow{\;f\;} S$$

as defined in (I, §6). This binary operation μ will be referred to as the *usual composition* in X.

(5) *Addition mod p.* Let p be a given positive integer and let X stand for the set Z_p of all nonnegative integers less than p. In other words, we have

$$X = \{0, 1, 2, \ldots, p - 1\}.$$

Then we may define a binary operation μ in this set X as follows. For any two numbers a and b in X, let the usual sum $a + b$ of these integers be divided by the positive integer p by means of the process called *long division*. Then we define $\mu(a, b)$ to be the remainder obtained in this way. In other words, $\mu(a, b)$ is the unique integer in $X = Z_p$ such that

$$a + b - \mu(a, b)$$

is a multiple of p. This binary operation μ in X will be referred to as the *addition mod p*.

(6) *Multiplication mod p.* Let p and X be the same as in **(5)**. We may define a binary operation μ in X as follows. For any two numbers a and b in X, let the usual product ab of these integers be divided by the positive integer p by means of long division. Then we define $\mu(a, b)$ to be the remainder obtained in this way. In other words, $\mu(a, b)$ is the unique integer in $X = Z_p$ such that

$$ab - \mu(a, b)$$

is a multiple of p. This binary operation μ in X will be referred to as the *multiplication mod p*.

(7) *Left projection.* Let X denote an arbitrarily given set. Then the *left projection* $\mu:X^2 \rightarrow X$ is defined by taking

$$\mu(a, b) = a$$

for each ordered pair of members a and b of X. By definition, μ is a binary operation in X.

(8) *Right projection.* Let X denote an arbitrarily given set. Then the *right projection* $\mu:X^2 \rightarrow X$ is defined by taking

$$\mu(a, b) = b$$

for each ordered pair of members a and b of X. By definition, μ is a binary operation in X.

In the present chapter, we will consider many binary operations in various sets. The composite of any two members a and b under such a binary operation μ will frequently be denoted by one of the following three notations:

$$a + b, \qquad ab, \qquad a \circ b,$$

although the binary operation μ may be very much different from those defined in Examples **(1)**–**(8)**.

If the composite $\mu(a, b)$ of a and b is denoted by $a + b$, then it will be called the *sum* of a and b. In this case, the binary operation μ is called an *addition* in the set X. In case the composite $\mu(a, b)$ is denoted by ab or $a \circ b$, it will be called the *product* of a and b. In this case, the binary operation μ is called a *multiplication* in X. We will use the multiplicative notation ab for the composite $\mu(a, b)$ unless there is a special reason for doing otherwise.

A binary operation in a given set X is said to be *associative* iff

$$(ab)c = a(bc)$$

holds for arbitrary members a, b, and c of the set X. In this particular case, the triple product abc is uniquely defined.

PROPOSITION 1.1. *In Examples (1)–(8), the usual subtraction is not associative and all other binary operations are associative.*

Proof. To see that the usual subtraction is not associative, let $a = b = c = 1$. Then we have $(a - b) - c = -1$ and $a - (b - c) = 1$. Hence

$$(a - b) - c \neq a - (b - c).$$

This proves that the usual subtraction is not associative.

The associativity of the usual addition and that of the usual multiplication are consequences of the associative laws of the number systems.

The associativity of the usual composition is a consequence of (I, 6.1).

To verify the associativity of the addition μ mod p, let a, b, and c denote arbitrary integers in Z_p. By definition, $\mu(a, b)$ is the unique integer in Z_p satisfying

$$a + b - \mu(a, b) = mp$$

for some $m \in Z$ and $\mu[\mu(a, b), c]$ is the unique integer $x \in Z_p$ satisfying

$$\mu(a, b) + c - x = np$$

for some $n \in Z$. It follows that x is the unique integer in Z_p satisfying the equation

$$a + b + c - x = kp$$

for some $k \in Z$. On the other hand, one can show that $\mu[a, \mu(b, c)]$ satisfies the same equation for some $k \in Z$. Hence we have

$$\mu[\mu(a, b), c] = \mu[a, \mu(b, c)].$$

The associativity of multiplication mod p can be verified similarly.

To verify the associativity of the left projection, let a, b, and c denote any three members of the set X. Then we have

$$(ab)c = ac = a, \qquad a(bc) = ab = a.$$

This implies $(ab)c = a(bc)$. Similarly, one can verify the associativity of the right projection. ‖

A binary operation in a set X is said to be *commutative* iff

$$ab = ba$$

for arbitrary members a and b of the set X.

PROPOSITION 1.2. *In the examples (1)–(8), the usual addition, the usual multiplication, the addition mod p, and the multiplication mod p are commutative; the remaining binary operations are not commutative except the trivial cases.*

Proof. The first half of the proposition is an immediate consequence of the commutative laws of the number systems.

To verify that the usual subtraction is not commutative, let $a = 1$ and $b = 2$. Then we have $a - b = -1$ and $b - a = 1$. Hence

$$a - b \neq b - a.$$

This proves that the usual subtraction is not commutative.

For the usual composition in the set X of all functions from a set S into itself, let us consider the nontrivial case where the set S consists of more than one member. In this case, let a and b denote any two distinct members of S. Define constant functions

$$f, g : S \rightarrow S$$

by taking $f(x) = a$ and $g(x) = b$ for each member x of S. Then we have the compositions

$$f \circ g = f, \qquad g \circ f = g.$$

Since $f \neq g$, it follows that

$$f \circ g \neq g \circ f.$$

This proves that the usual composition is not commutative whenever the set S consists of more than one member.

As to the trivial case where the set S is a singleton, the usual composition in the set X of all functions from S into itself is obviously commutative, since in this case X is also a singleton.

For the left projection in a set X, let us first consider the nontrivial case where the set X consists of more than one member. In this case, let a and b denote any two distinct members of X. Then we have $ab = a$ and $ba = b$. Since $a \neq b$, it follows that

$$ab \neq ba.$$

This proves that the left projection in X is not commutative whenever X consists of more than one member. As to the trivial case where X is a singleton, the left projection in X is obviously commutative.

Similarly, one can verify that the right projection in a set X is not commutative unless X consists of a single member. In case X is a singleton, the right projection is obviously commutative.‖

Now let us consider an arbitrary set X together with a given binary operation in the set X. A member e of the set X is called a *left unit* (of the binary operation) iff

$$ex = x$$

is true for each member $x \in X$. Similarly, a member $e \in X$ is called a *right unit* iff

$$xe = x$$

is true for each member $x \in X$. If a member e of X is both a left unit and a right unit, then it will be referred to as a *unit*, or a *neutral element*, of the given binary operation.

PROPOSITION 1.3. *In Examples* (1)–(8), *the integer* 0 *is a unit of the usual addition and of the addition mod p, the integer* 1 *is a unit of the usual multiplication and of the multiplication mod p, and the identity function i on the set S is a unit of the usual composition. The usual subtraction has a unique right unit, namely* 0, *but has no left unit. If X is not a singleton, then the left (right) projection in X has no left (right) unit but every member of X is a right (left) unit.*

The verification of (1.3) is straightforward and hence omitted.

THEOREM 1.4. *If a binary operation in a set X has a left unit u and a right unit v, then we have $u = v$.*

Proof. Let us consider the product uv in the set X. From the definition of left units, it follows that $uv = v$. Similarly, from the definition of right units, it follows that $uv = u$. This implies $u = v$.∥

The following corollary is a direct consequence of (1.4).

COROLLARY 1.5. *A binary operation in a set X can have at most one unit.*

An element x of the set X is called an *idempotent* with respect to the given binary operation iff

$$x^2 = x$$

holds. In particular, each left unit is an idempotent and so is each right unit. Consequently, every unit is an idempotent.

In case the set X is finite, it is convenient to tabulate the products of a given binary operation in X by means of a *multiplication table*. If

$$x_1, x_2, \ldots, x_n$$

are the members of the set X, then the multiplication table is of the form of a square array of X, consisting of n rows and n columns both labeled by $x_1, x_2, \ldots, x_n$ in this order. The member at the intersection of the ith row and the jth column is the product $x_i x_j$.

For example, the multiplication tables of the addition mod 3 and the multiplication mod 3 are as follows:

+	0	1	2
0	0	1	2
1	1	2	0
2	2	0	1

×	0	1	2
0	0	0	0
1	0	1	2
2	0	2	1.

EXERCISES

1A. Let $X = \{a, b, c\}$ and consider the binary operation in X defined by the following multiplication table:

	a	b	c
a	a	c	b
b	c	b	a
c	b	a	$c.$

Prove that this binary operation in X is commutative but not associative.

1B. Consider the set $X = 2^S$ of all subsets of a given set S. Show that union and intersection of sets define two binary operations in X which are both associative and commutative. Verify that the empty subset $\square$ of S is a unit for union and that the subset S of S is a unit for intersection.

1C. Let S denote any given set which contains more than two members. Consider the set X of all bijective functions from S onto itself. Prove that the usual composition defines a binary operation in X which is associative but not commutative. Furthermore, show that the identity function on S is a unit of this binary operation.

1D. Let X denote the set which consists of two members denoted by T and F, respectively. Show that the *Boolean addition* and the *Boolean multiplication* defined by the following tables

$+$	T	F
T	T	T
F	T	F

$\times$	T	F
T	T	F
F	F	F

are commutative and associative binary operations. Prove that F is a unit of the Boolean addition and that T is a unit of the Boolean multiplication.

2. SEMIGROUPS

By a *semigroup*, we mean a set X furnished with an associative binary operation μ. The set X will be called the *underlying set* of the semigroup, and μ will be called the *binary operation* of the semigroup. To simplify the notation, the semigroup will be denoted by the same symbol, X, as its underlying set.

According to (1.1), each of the binary operations in Examples **(1)**–**(8)**, except the usual subtraction, makes the set X a semigroup. From Examples **(7)** and **(8)**, we see that every set X can be the underlying set of a semigroup.

A semigroup X is said to be *commutative* iff its binary operation is commutative. In other words, a semigroup X is commutative iff

$$ab = ba$$

holds for arbitrary members a and b of X.

According to (1.2), the semigroups in Examples **(1)**, **(2)**, **(5)**, and **(6)** are commutative, and those in Examples **(4)**, **(7)**, and **(8)** are not commutative except for the trivial cases.

A semigroup X is called a *monoid* iff its binary operation has a unit e. According to (1.5), e is the only unit of the binary operation and will be called the *unit* of the monoid X.

According to (1.3), the semigroups in Examples **(1)**, **(2)**, **(4)**, **(5)**, and **(6)** are monoids.

Let W denote any given subset of a semigroup X. Then we say that W is *stable* with respect to the binary operation of the semigroup X iff $ab \in W$ holds for all members a and b of W. For any stable subset W of a semigroup X, the restriction

$$\nu = \mu \mid W^2$$

of the binary operation $\mu : X^2 \to X$ of the semigroup X on the Cartesian square $W^2 \subset X^2$ defines an associative binary operation in the set W. This binary operation $\sqrt{}$ makes the set W a semigroup which will be called a *subsemigroup* of the semigroup X.

In case the given semigroup X is a monoid and the unit e of X is contained in the subsemigroup W of X, W is a monoid with e as unit and will be called a *submonoid* of the given monoid X.

EXAMPLES OF SUBSEMIGROUPS AND SUBMONOIDS

(a) The additive semigroup N of all natural numbers is a subsemigroup of each of the additive monoids Z, Q, R, and C in Example **(1)** of §1.

(b) The multiplicative monoid N of all natural numbers and the multiplicative monoid $\{1, -1\}$ are submonoids of each of the multiplicative monoids Z, Q, R, and C in Example **(2)** of §1.

(c) Let S denote an arbitrarily given nonempty set. Then the set P of all bijective functions from S onto itself is a submonoid of the monoid X of all functions from S into itself in Example **(4)** of §1. This monoid P will be called the *permutation monoid* of the given set S.

By a *homomorphism* of a semigroup X into a semigroup Y, we mean a function

$$f:X \to Y$$

which preserves products; that is to say,

$$f(ab) = f(a)f(b)$$

holds for all members a and b of X.

EXAMPLES OF HOMOMORPHISMS

(A) If X is a subsemigroup of a semigroup Y, then the inclusion function

$$i:X \subset Y$$

obviously preserves products and hence is a homomorphism of X into Y. This homomorphism i will be referred to as the *inclusion homomorphism*. In particular, the identity function on any semigroup X is a homomorphism of X into itself which will be called the *identity homomorphism* of the semigroup X.

(B) Let X denote any of the number systems Z, Q, R, and C. For any given number $a \in X$, the function

$$h_a:X \to X$$

from X into itself defined by

$$h_a(x) = ax$$

for every number $x \in X$ is a homomorphism of the additive monoid X into itself.

(C) The exponential function

$$p:R \to C$$

from the set R of all real numbers into the set C of all complex numbers defined by

$$p(x) = e^{2\pi x i} = \cos (2\pi x) + i \sin (2\pi x)$$

for every $x \in R$ is a homomorphism of the additive monoid R into the multiplicative monoid C.

(D) Let $a \neq 1$ denote any positive real number. The function

$$q:P \to R$$

from the set P of all positive real numbers into the set R of all real numbers defined by

$$q(x) = \log_a (x)$$

for every $x \in P$ is a homomorphism of the multiplicative monoid P into the additive monoid R.

(E) Consider the additive monoids $\mathcal{Z}$ and $\mathcal{Z}_p$ of integers and integers mod p, respectively. The function

$$r:\mathcal{Z} \to \mathcal{Z}_p$$

defined by taking $r(x)$, for every $x \in \mathcal{Z}$, to be the uniquely determined integer in $\mathcal{Z}_p$ such that

$$x - r(x)$$

is a multiple of the integer p, is a homomorphism.

Let $h:X \to Y$ be an arbitrarily given homomorphism of a semigroup X into a semigroup Y. If h is injective, it is called a *monomorphism;* if h is surjective, it is called an *epimorphism;* if h is bijective, it is called an *isomorphism.* Two semigroups X and Y are said to be *isomorphic*, in symbols

$$X \approx Y,$$

iff an isomorphism $h:X \to Y$ exists. Finally, a homomorphism $h:X \to X$ of a semigroup X into itself is called an *endomorphism* of X, and bijective endomorphisms of a semigroup X are called *automorphisms* of X.

In Examples (A)–(E), the inclusion homomorphism i in (A) is a monomorphism. The homomorphism r in (E) is an epimorphism. The homomorphism q in (D) is an isomorphism and hence the multiplicative monoid P is isomorphic to the additive monoid R. The homomorphism h_a in (B) is an endomorphism and the identity homomorphism in (A) is an automorphism.

THEOREM 2.1. *Let X, Y, and $\mathcal{Z}$ be semigroups. The composition*

$$g \circ f:X \to \mathcal{Z}$$

of any two given homomorphisms $f:X \to Y$ and $g:Y \to \mathcal{Z}$ is a homomorphism.

Proof. Let a and b denote any two members of the semigroup X. Then it follows from the definition of homomorphisms that we have

$$(g \circ f)(ab) = g[f(ab)] = g[f(a)f(b)]$$
$$= g[f(a)]g[f(b)] = [(g \circ f)(a)][(g \circ f)(b)].$$

This proves that $g \circ f$ is a homomorphism.$\|$

Since, according to (I, §6), the composition of any two injective functions is injective and the composition of any two surjective functions is surjective, we have the following corollary of (2.1).

COROLLARY 2.2. *If f and g are monomorphisms, then so is their composition g ∘ f; if f and g are epimorphisms, then so is g ∘ f.*

As a partial converse of (2.2), we have the following theorem which is a direct consequence of (I, 6.3).

THEOREM 2.3. *For the composition $h = g \circ f$ of any two homomorphisms $f : X \to Y$ and $g : Y \to Z$, the following two statements are true:*

(i) *If h is a monomorphism, so is f.*
(ii) *If h is an epimorphism, so is g.*

Now let us establish the following theorem.

THEOREM 2.4. *If $h : X \to Y$ is an arbitrary homomorphism of a semigroup X into a semigroup Y, then the image $h(A)$ of any subsemigroup A of X is a subsemigroup of Y and the inverse image $h^{-1}(B)$ of any subsemigroup B of Y is a subsemigroup of X.*

Proof. First, let us prove that $h(A)$ is a subsemigroup of Y. For this purpose, let p and q denote any two members of the image $h(A)$. Then there are members r and s of A with $h(r) = p$ and $h(s) = q$. Since A is a subsemigroup of X and h is a homomorphism, we have

$$pq = h(r)h(s) = h(rs) \; \epsilon \; h(A).$$

Since p and q are arbitrary elements of $h(A)$, this proves that $h(A)$ is a subsemigroup of Y.

Next, let us prove that $h^{-1}(B)$ is a subsemigroup of X. Let u and v denote arbitrary members of $h^{-1}(B)$. It follows from the definition of the inverse image $h^{-1}(B)$ that $h(u)$ and $h(v)$ are members of B. Since B is a subsemigroup of Y and h is a homomorphism, we have

$$h(uv) = h(u)h(v) \; \epsilon \; B.$$

Therefore, $uv \; \epsilon \; h^{-1}(B)$. Since u and v are arbitrary members of $h^{-1}(B)$, this proves that $h^{-1}(B)$ is a subsemigroup of X.‖

For example, the image $p(R)$ of the exponential homomorphism p in Example (**C**) is a subsemigroup of the multiplicative monoid C of all complex numbers. By the definition of p, one can easily see that $p(R)$ is the unit circumference S^1 of the complex plane C; in symbols,

$$p(R) = S^1 = \{z \; \epsilon \; C \mid |z| = 1\}.$$

Since this subsemigroup S^1 of the monoid C contains the unit 1 of C, S^1 is a submonoid of C.

Throughout the rest of the present section, let

$$h : X \longrightarrow Y$$

denote an arbitrarily given homomorphism of a semigroup X into a semigroup Y.

LEMMA 2.5. *If a member $a \in X$ is an idempotent, then so is the member $h(a)$ of Y.*

Proof. According to the definition of an idempotent, we have $a^2 = a$. Then it follows that

$$[h(a)]^2 = h(a)h(a) = h(a^2) = h(a)$$

holds since h is a homomorphism. This proves that $h(a)$ is an idempotent.‖

LEMMA 2.6. *If X is a monoid with e as its unit, then $h(X)$ is a monoid with $h(e)$ as its unit.*

Proof. According to (2.4), $h(X)$ is a subsemigroup of Y. Therefore, it suffices to prove that $h(e)$ is a unit of the semigroup $h(X)$. For this purpose, let b denote any member of $h(X)$. By the definition of the image $h(X)$, there exists a member $a \in X$ with $h(a) = b$. Since e is the unit of X and h is a homomorphism, we have

$$[h(e)]b = h(e)h(a) = h(ea) = h(a) = b,$$
$$b[h(e)] = h(a)h(e) = h(ae) = h(a) = b.$$

Since b is an arbitrary member of $h(X)$, this proves that $h(e)$ is a unit of $h(X)$.‖

Next assume that X and Y are monoids with their units denoted by $u \in X$ and $v \in Y$, respectively. According to (2.5), $h(u)$ is an idempotent of Y but is not necessarily the unit v of Y.

For a counterexample, let us consider the constant function

$$\theta : \mathcal{Z} \longrightarrow \mathcal{Z}$$

defined by $\theta(x) = 0$ for every integer x. Then θ is an endomorphism of the multiplicative monoid $\mathcal{Z}$. Here, $h(1) = 0$ is an idempotent of $\mathcal{Z}$ but is not the unit 1 of $\mathcal{Z}$.

Because of this fact, we will introduce the notion of a proper homomorphism as follows.

A homomorphism $h : X \longrightarrow Y$ of a monoid X into a monoid Y is said to be *proper* iff h sends the unit of X to the unit of Y; in symbols,

$$h(u) = v.$$

THEOREM 2.7. *For an arbitrarily given homomorphism*

$$h:X \rightarrow Y$$

of a monoid X into a monoid Y, the following statements are equivalent:

(i) h *is proper.*
(ii) $h(X)$ *is a submonoid of Y.*
(iii) *The inverse image $h^{-1}(v)$ of the unit v of Y is a submonoid of X.*

Proof. **(i)** $\Rightarrow$ **(ii)**. Because of $h(u) = v$, the unit v of Y is contained in $h(X)$. By (2.4), $h(X)$ is a subsemigroup of Y. Consequently, $h(X)$ is a submonoid of Y.

(ii) $\Rightarrow$ **(iii)**. By (2.6) and (ii), both $h(u)$ and v are units of the monoid $h(X)$. Hence we have $h(u) = v$. This implies that u is contained in the subsemigroup $h^{-1}(v)$ of X. Hence $h^{-1}(v)$ is a submonoid of X.

(iii) $\Rightarrow$ **(i)**. By (iii), the unit u of X is contained in $h^{-1}(v)$. Hence we have $h(u) = v$. This proves that h is proper.‖

COROLLARY 2.8. *Every epimorphism $h:X \rightarrow Y$ of a monoid X onto a monoid Y is proper.*

Proof. Since h is an epimorphism, we have $h(X) = Y$. Hence (2.8) is a consequence of (ii) $\Rightarrow$ (i) in (2.7).‖

The statements **(ii)** and **(iii)** suggest that the subsets $h(X)$ and $h^{-1}(v)$ of the monoids Y and X respectively are important and deserve special names. Thus, $h(X)$ will be called the *image* of the homomorphism h and $h^{-1}(v)$ will be called the *kernel* of h; in symbols, these will be denoted by

$$\text{Im}(h) = h(X)$$
$$\text{Ker}(h) = h^{-1}(v).$$

If h is an isomorphism, then we obviously have

$$\text{Im}(h) = Y$$
$$\text{Ker}(h) = \{u\}.$$

However, the converse of this statement is not always true.

EXERCISES

2A. Prove that the intersection of any family of subsemigroups of a semigroup X is a subsemigroup of X and that the intersection of any family of submonoids of a monoid X is a submonoid of X.

2B. Let X denote any semigroup and e an object which is not in X. Extend the binary operation of X over the set

$$X^* = X \cup \{e\}$$

by taking $e^2 = e$ and $ex = x = xe$ for every $x \in X$. Prove that this binary operation in X^* makes X^* a monoid with e as its unit and X as a subsemigroup but not as a submonoid.

2C. Prove that every homomorphism $h:A \to B$ of a semigroup A into a semigroup B extends to a unique proper homomorphism $h^*:A^* \to B^*$ of the monoids A^* and B^* as defined in 2B. Prove that the kernel of h^* consists of the unit u of A^* as its only member. Hence, if h is an epimorphism but not an isomorphism, then h^* is not an isomorphism, although we have

$$\text{Im}(h^*) = B^*$$
$$\text{Ker}(h)^* = \{u\}.$$

2D. Let $h:X \to Y$ denote any isomorphism of a semigroup X onto a semigroup Y. Prove that the inverse function $h^{-1}:Y \to X$ is also an isomorphism.

2E. Prove that the restriction $h \mid A$ of a homomorphism $h:X \to Y$ on any subsemigroup A of X is a homomorphism of A into Y. If h is a monomorphism, then so is $h \mid A$.

3. GROUPS

Consider an arbitrary monoid X with unit e. Let x denote any member of the monoid X.

A member u of the monoid X is said to be a *left inverse* of x iff

$$ux = e$$

holds. Similarly, a member v of X is said to be a *right inverse* of x iff

$$xv = e$$

holds. By an *inverse* of x, we mean a member y of X which is both a left inverse and a right inverse of x. In case x has an inverse in X, we say that x is *invertible*. Clearly, the unit e of the given monoid X is invertible.

LEMMA 3.1. *If a member x of a monoid X has a left inverse u and a right inverse v, then we have $u = v$.*

Proof. Consider the triple product

$$w = uxv$$

in the monoid X. Since u is a left inverse of x and v is a right inverse of x, we have

$$u = ue = u(xv) = w = (ux)v = ev = v.$$

This proves the lemma.‖

COROLLARY 3.2. *Every invertible member of a monoid has a unique inverse.*

We will denote the unique inverse of any invertible member x of a monoid X by the symbol x^{-1}.

By a *group*, we mean a monoid of which every member is invertible.

EXAMPLES

(1) The additive monoids Z, Q, R, and C of the number systems are groups, but their multiplicative monoids are not groups. The submonoids $Q \setminus \{0\}$, $R \setminus \{0\}$, and $C \setminus \{0\}$ of the multiplicative monoids Q, R, and C, respectively, are groups.

(2) The additive monoid Z_p of all integers mod p is a group, while the multiplicative monoid Z_p is not a group whenever $p > 1$.

(3) The circle monoid S^1 which consists of all complex numbers z with $|z| = 1$ under the usual multiplication of complex numbers is a group and is known as the *circle group*.

(4) The monoid X of all functions from a given set S into itself under the usual composition is not a group whenever S consists of more than one member. However, the submonoid W of X, which consists of all bijective functions, is a group. This group W is known as the *permutation group* of the set S and will be denoted by $P(S)$.

(5) The monoid E of all endomorphisms of a given semigroup S under the usual composition is, in general, not a group. However, the submonoid A of E which consists of all automorphisms of S is a group. This group A is known as the *automorphism group* of S and will be denoted by $A(S)$.

THEOREM 3.3. *A semigroup X is a group iff the following two conditions are satisfied:*

(i) *The existence of a left unit: there exists a member e of X such that $ex = x$ holds for every member x of X.*

(ii) *The existence of a left inverse: for every member x of X, there exists a member u of X satisfying $ux = e$.*

Proof. Since the necessity of the conditions is obvious, it remains to establish the sufficiency. Thus, we assume that the conditions are satisfied.

Choose a left unit e of X by (i). Let x denote an arbitrary member of X. According to (ii), we can choose a member u of X with $ux = e$.

Next, applying (**ii**) to this member u of X, we get a member v of X with $vu = e$. Then we have

$$xu = exu = vuxu = veu = vu = e$$

and, therefore, u is also a right inverse of x. On the other hand, we also have

$$xe = x(ux) = (xu)x = ex = x.$$

This proves that e is also a right unit of X and hence e is a unit of X. Since we have proved that u is an inverse of X, this completes the proof.‖

Obviously a similar theorem holds with "left unit" and "left inverse" replaced by "right unit" and "right inverse."

THEOREM 3.4. *A nonempty semigroup X is a group iff the equations*

$$xa = b, \qquad ay = b$$

are solvable for x and y in X, where a and b are arbitrary members of X.

Proof. Necessity. Assume that X is a group. Then the equations $xa = b$ and $ay = b$ have uniquely determined solutions

$$x = ba^{-1}, \qquad y = a^{-1}b.$$

Sufficiency. Since X is not empty, there is a member a of X. It follows from the condition that there exists a member e of X with $ea = a$. To prove that e is a left unit of X, let x denote any member of X. According to the condition, there exists a member y of X with $ay = x$. Then we have

$$ex = e(ay) = (ea)y = ay = x.$$

This proves that e is a left unit of X. Next, to prove the existence of the left inverse, let x denote any member of X. According to the condition, there exists a member u of X with $ux = e$. Hence u is a left inverse of x. By (3.3), it follows that X is a group.‖

Hereafter, the unit of a group will be called the *neutral element*.

THEOREM 3.5. *The neutral element of a group is its only idempotent.*

Proof. Let x denote an arbitrary idempotent of a group X with neutral element e. According to the definition of idempotents, we have $x^2 = x$. If we multiply both sides of this equation by x^{-1}, we get

$$x = x^2 x^{-1} = xx^{-1} = e.$$

This proves that x must be the neutral element e.‖

THEOREM 3.6. *For any two elements a and b of a group X, we have*

$$(ab)^{-1} = b^{-1}a^{-1}.$$

Proof. In view of the following two products:

$$(ab)(b^{-1}a^{-1}) = a(bb^{-1})a^{-1} = aa^{-1} = e,$$
$$(b^{-1}a^{-1})(ab) = b^{-1}(a^{-1}a)b = b^{-1}b = e,$$

we obtain $(ab)^{-1} = b^{-1}a^{-1}.\|$

Commutative groups are called *Abelian groups*. For example, the groups in (1)–(3) are Abelian groups, while those in (4) and (5) are not commutative in general.

In an Abelian group X, the binary operation is usually denoted by the symbol $+$ of addition. If this is the case, then the neutral element of X is denoted by 0 and is called the *zero* of the Abelian group X. Furthermore, the inverse of any element x of X is denoted by $-x$ and is called the *negation* of the given element x.

A subsemigroup A of a semigroup X may happen to be a group with respect to the same binary operation. If this is the case, then A is said to be a *subgroup* of the semigroup X.

EXAMPLES OF SUBGROUPS

(a) Let X denote any monoid with e as the neutral element. Then the submonoid $\{e\}$ of X is obviously a group and hence is a subgroup of X.

(b) Let X denote any of the number systems Q, R, and C. Then the submonoid $X\backslash\{0\}$ is a subgroup of the multiplicative monoid X.

(c) The submonoid $\{1, -1\}$ of the multiplicative monoid Z of all integers is a subgroup of Z.

(d) The permutation group $P(S)$ of a set S is a subgroup of the monoid $F(S)$ of all functions from S into itself.

(e) The automorphism group $A(S)$ of a semigroup S is a subgroup of the monoid $E(S)$ of all endomorphisms of the semigroup S.

In particular, we are very much interested in the case where the given semigroup X itself is a group.

THEOREM 3.7. *If A is an arbitrary subset of a group X, then A forms a subgroup of X iff the following three conditions are satisfied:*

(i) *The neutral element e of the group X is contained in A.*
(ii) *For each member x of A, the inverse x^{-1} is contained in A.*
(iii) *For any two members x and y of A, the product xy is contained in A.*

Proof. Necessity. Assume that A is a subgroup of X. Then, by definition, A must have a neutral element u. Since $u^2 = u$ holds, u is an idempotent of X. According to (3.5), we have $u = e$. This implies (**i**).

Next, let x denote an arbitrary member of A. Since A is a group, x has a left inverse $u \in A$. Thus we have $ux = e$. If we multiply both sides of $ux = e$ by x^{-1} on the right, we get $u = x^{-1}$. This implies (**ii**).

Since A is a subsemigroup of X, (**iii**) holds. This proves the necessity.

Sufficiency. Assume A to be a subset of X which satisfies the conditions. By (**iii**), A is a subsemigroup of X. Because of (**i**) and (**ii**), A is a group. Therefore, A is a subgroup of X.‖

COROLLARY 3.8. *A nonempty subsemigroup A of a group X is a subgroup of X iff, for every member x of A, the inverse x^{-1} is contained in A.*

Proof. Since A is a subsemigroup of X, the condition (**iii**) of (3.7) holds. Since A is nonempty and since (**iii**) of (3.7) holds, it follows that (**ii**) implies (**i**). Hence, (3.7) implies (3.8).‖

By a simple application of (3.8), one can easily see that, in the additive group R of all real numbers, the subsemigroup Z of all integers is a subgroup of R but the subsemigroup N of all natural numbers is not a subgroup of R.

Since every group is a semigroup, the terminology of homomorphism, etc., introduced in the preceding section applies to groups as well as semigroups.

LEMMA 3.9. *Every homomorphism $h : X \to Y$ of a group X into a group Y is proper; that is, h sends the neutral element e_X of X into the neutral element e_Y of Y.*

Proof. According to (2.5), $h(e_X)$ is an idempotent of Y. Since Y is a group, it follows from (3.5) that $h(e_X)$ is the neutral element e_Y of Y.‖

LEMMA 3.10. *If $h : X \to Y$ is a homomorphism of a group X into a group Y, then we have*

$$h(x^{-1}) = [h(x)]^{-1}$$

for every member x of the group X.

Proof. Since h is a homomorphism, we have

$$h(x)h(x^{-1}) = h(xx^{-1}) = h(e_X)$$

for every member x of X. According to (3.9), we have $h(e_X) = e_Y$. Hence it follows that

$$h(x^{-1}) = [h(x)]^{-1}$$

holds for every member x of X.‖

THEOREM 3.11. *For any homomorphism $h:X \to Y$ of a group X into a group Y, the image $\text{Im}(h)$ is a subgroup of Y and the kernel $\text{Ker}(h)$ is a subgroup of X.*

Proof. According to (3.9), h is proper. In view of (2.7), this implies that $\text{Im}(h)$ is a submonoid of Y and $\text{Ker}(h)$ is a submonoid of X.

To prove that $\text{Im}(h)$ is a subgroup of Y, let y denote any member of $\text{Im}(h)$. By definition of $\text{Im}(h) = h(X)$, there exists a member x of X with $y = h(x)$. According to (3.10), we have

$$y^{-1} = h(x^{-1}) \, \epsilon \, h(X) = \text{Im}(h).$$

Because of (3.8), this implies that $\text{Im}(h)$ is a subgroup of Y.

To prove that $\text{Ker}(h)$ is a subgroup of X, let x denote any member of $\text{Ker}(h)$. Then it follows from the definition of $\text{Ker}(h)$ that $h(x) = e_Y$ holds. According to (3.10), we have

$$h(x^{-1}) = e_Y^{-1} = e_Y.$$

This implies $x^{-1} \, \epsilon \, \text{Ker}(h)$. By (3.8), $\text{Ker}(h)$ is a subgroup of X.‖

THEOREM 3.12. *A homomorphism $h:X \to Y$ of a group X into a group Y is a monomorphism iff $\text{Ker}(h) = \{e_X\}$.*

Proof. Necessity. Assume that h is a monomorphism. According to (3.9), we have

$$e_X \, \epsilon \, h^{-1}(e_Y) = \text{Ker}(h).$$

By the definition of a monomorphism, h is injective. Hence $\text{Ker}(h)$ cannot contain more than one member of X. Consequently, we have $\text{Ker}(h) = \{e_X\}$.

Sufficiency. Assume $\text{Ker}(h) = \{e_X\}$. To prove that h is a monomorphism, let a and b denote any two members of X such that $h(a) = h(b)$ holds. By (3.10) and the fact that h is a homomorphism, we have

$$h(ab^{-1}) = h(a)h(b^{-1}) = h(a)[h(b)]^{-1} = e_Y.$$

Therefore ab^{-1} is a member of $\text{Ker}(h)$. Because $\text{Ker}(h) = \{e_X\}$, this implies $ab^{-1} = e_X$. Hence we have $a = b$. This proves that h is a monomorphism.‖

In the remainder of the section, let X denote any given group with e as its neutral element. For every member a of X, define a function

$$T_a:X \to X$$

by taking $T_a(x) = ax$ for every $x \, \epsilon \, X$. This function T_a of X into itself is known as the *left translation* of the group X by the given member a of X.

LEMMA 3.13. *For every member a of X, the left translation T_a of the group X is bijective.*

Proof. First let us prove that T_a is injective. For this purpose, let u and v denote any two members of X with $T_a(u) = T_a(v)$. Then it follows from the definition of T_a that we have $au = av$. By multiplying with a^{-1} on the left of both sides of this equality, we obtain $u = v$. This proves that T_a is injective.

Next, let us prove that T_a is surjective. For this purpose, let y denote any member of X. Let $x = a^{-1}y \in X$. Then we have

$$T_a(x) = ax = aa^{-1}y = y.$$

Therefore, T_a is surjective. ‖

By (3.13), T_a is a member of the permutation group $P(X)$ of the set X. Define a function

$$j: X \to P(X)$$

by taking $j(a) = T_a$ for every $a \in X$.

THEOREM 3.14. *The function j is a monomorphism of the group X into the permutation group $P(X)$ of the set X.*

Proof. First let us prove that j is a homomorphism. For this purpose, let a and b denote any two members of X. Then, for an arbitrary member x of X, we have

$$[j(ab)](x) = T_{ab}(x) = abx = T_a[T_b(x)]$$
$$= [T_a \circ T_b](x) = [j(a) \circ j(b)](x).$$

Since x is arbitrary, this implies

$$j(ab) = j(a) \circ j(b).$$

This proves that j is a homomorphism.

Next let us prove that j is a monomorphism. For this purpose, let a denote any member of the kernel $\mathrm{Ker}(j)$. By the definition of kernel, this implies that $j(a) = T_a$ is the identity function on X. Hence we have

$$a^2 = aa = T_a(a) = a.$$

Therefore, a is an idempotent of the group X. By (3.5), this implies that a is the neutral element e of the group X. Hence $\mathrm{Ker}(j) = \{e\}$. According to (3.12), j is a monomorphism. ‖

COROLLARY 3.15. *Every group X is isomorphic to a subgroup $j(X)$ of the permutation group $P(X)$ of the set X.*

EXERCISES

3A. Prove that the cancellation laws hold in any group X; that is, for arbitrarily given members a, b, c of X, the following three statements are equivalent:

    (i) $a = b$

    (ii) $ca = cb$

    (iii) $ac = bc$.

3B. Let a denote any member of a group X. Prove that

    (i) $a^m a^n = a^{m+n}$,

    (ii) $(a^m)^n = a^{mn}$

hold for all integers m and n with a^0 standing for the unit e of the group X.

3C. Prove that a nonempty subset A of a group X is a subgroup of X iff $bc^{-1} \epsilon A$ holds for all members b and c of A.

3D. Prove that the intersection of any family of subgroups of a group X is a subgroup of X. In particular, for any subset S of a group X, the intersection of all subgroups containing S is a subgroup of X, called the *subgroup of X generated by S*.

3E. A group X is said to be *cyclic* iff it is generated by a singleton subset $\{g\}$ of X; in this case, g is called a *generator* of X. Prove that every subgroup of a cyclic group is cyclic.

3F. Let x denote any given member of a group X. Define a function $h: \mathcal{Z} \to X$ from the additive group $\mathcal{Z}$ of integers into X by taking $h(n) = x^n$ for each integer $n \epsilon \mathcal{Z}$. Prove that h is a homomorphism and that $\text{Im}(h)$ is the cyclic subgroup of X generated by $\{x\}$.

3G. Prove that a nonempty finite semigroup X is a group iff, for any members a, b, c of X, the following two cancellation laws hold:

    (i) $ca = cb$ implies $a = b$

    (ii) $ac = bc$ implies $a = b$.

As an application, prove that, for any prime number p, the set $\mathcal{Z}_p \setminus \{0\}$ of the first $p - 1$ natural numbers $1, 2, \ldots, p - 1$ forms a group with respect to the multiplication mod p.

4. RINGS, INTEGRAL DOMAINS, AND FIELDS

So far, we have studied algebraic structures with only one binary operation. In the present section, we are concerned with those algebraic structures which have two given binary operations.

By a *ring*, we mean a nonempty set X furnished with two binary operations called *addition* and *multiplication*, respectively, such that the following three conditions are satisfied:

(**R1**) The members of X form an Abelian group with respect to addition.

(**R2**) The members of X form a semigroup with respect to multiplication.

(**R3**) For arbitrary members a, b, c of X, the following two *distributive laws* hold:

$$a(b + c) = ab + ac,$$
$$(b + c)a = ba + ca.$$

EXAMPLES OF RINGS

(**1**) Let X denote any of the number systems Z, Q, R, and C. Then the members of X form a ring with respect to the usual addition and the usual multiplication in X.

(**2**) Let p denote any positive integer. Then the integers $Z_p = \{0, 1, \ldots, p - 1\}$ mod p form a ring with respect to the addition mod p and the multiplication mod p in Z_p. This ring Z_p will be referred to as the *ring of integers mod p*.

(**3**) Let S be any given set and let X denote any of the number systems Z, Q, R, and C. Then the set $F = X^S$ of all functions $f : S \to X$ forms a ring with respect to the addition and the multiplication defined for arbitrary g, $h \in F$ by

$$(g + h)(s) = g(s) + h(s),$$
$$(gh)(s) = g(s)h(s),$$

for every member s of the set S. This ring F is called the *ring of all X-valued functions on the set S*. The addition and the multiplication in F are called the *functional addition* and the *functional multiplication*, respectively.

(**4**) Let X be any given Abelian group denoted additively. Then the set $E = E(X)$ of all endomorphisms of the Abelian group X forms a ring with respect to the addition and the multiplication defined for arbitrary g, $h \in E$ by

$$(g + h)(x) = g(x) + h(x),$$
$$(gh)(x) = g[h(x)],$$

for every member x of the Abelian group X. This ring E is known as the *ring of all endomorphisms* of X.

(**5**) Consider an arbitrarily given Abelian group X denoted additively. Give X the *trivial multiplication;* that is, the binary operation X defined by

$ab = 0$ for all members a and b of X. Then X becomes a ring. This ring will be called the *ring of the Abelian group X with trivial multiplication.*

Because of Example (5), the additive Abelian group of a ring can be any given Abelian group.

By imposing various conditions on the multiplicative semigroup, we will obtain different types of rings.

A ring X is said to be *commutative* iff its multiplicative semigroup is commutative.

In the preceding examples, the rings in (1), (2), (3), and (5) are commutative while the ring $E = E(X)$ of all endomorphisms of an Abelian group X is not commutative in general.

By a *ring with unit*, we mean a ring X in which the multiplicative semigroup is a monoid. In this case, the unique unit of this multiplicative monoid will be called the *unit* (or the *identity*) of the ring X and will be denoted by the symbol 1. If X consists of more than one member, then the unit 1 of X must be different from the *zero* 0 of the additive Abelian group of X. In fact, we have the following lemma.

LEMMA 4.1.   *In an arbitrarily given ring X, we have*

$$0x = 0 = x0$$

for every member x of X.

Proof. Since 0 is the neutral element of the additive Abelian group X, we have

$$0 + 0 = 0.$$

Let x denote an arbitrary member of X. Applying the distributive law (R3), we obtain

$$0x = (0 + 0)x = 0x + 0x.$$

It follows that $0x = 0$ holds. Similarly, one can prove $x0 = 0$.‖

In the preceding examples, the rings in (1)–(4) are rings with unit while the ring X in (5) has no unit unless X is a singleton. The units of the rings in (1) and (2) are the number 1. The unit of the ring F in (3) is the constant function 1 which sends the whole set S into the unit 1 of the ring X. The unit of the ring E in (4) is the identity endomorphism of the Abelian group X.

If the product ab of two nonzero members a and b of a ring X is the zero 0 of X, then we say that a and b are *divisors of zero* in the given ring X.

For example, let $n = pq$ where p and q denote two positive integers greater than 1. Then both p and q are divisors of zero in the ring Z_n of integers mod n.

The following lemma is obvious.

LEMMA 4.2. *A ring X has no divisor of zero iff $X\backslash\{0\}$ forms a subsemigroup of the multiplicative semigroup.*

For example, the ring $\mathcal{Z}_n$ of integers mod n, $n > 1$, has no divisor of zero iff n is a prime.

Next, let us establish the following lemma.

LEMMA 4.3. *A ring X has no divisor of zero iff the cancellation laws hold in X for every nonzero member x of X; that is, iff for any two members a and b of X, the following two statements are true:*

(i) $xa = xb$ *implies* $a = b$.
(ii) $ax = bx$ *implies* $a = b$.

Proof. Necessity. Assume that X has no divisor of zero. To prove (i), let us assume that $xa = xb$. By (R3), we have

$$x(a - b) = xa - xb = 0.$$

Since $x \neq 0$ and X has no divisor of zero, this implies $a - b = 0$. Hence we obtain $a = b$. This proves (i). Similarly, we can prove (ii).

Sufficiency. Assume (i) and (ii) for every nonzero member x of X. To prove that X has no divisor of zero, let us assume that the product ab of two nonzero members a and b of X is 0. We will derive a contradiction. Since $a0 = 0$ holds according to (4.1), we obtain $ab = a0$. Since $a \neq 0$, it follows from (i) that $b = 0$ holds. This contradicts the assumption $b \neq 0$ and completes the proof.‖

By an *integral domain*, we mean a ring with unit which has no divisor of zero. It follows from (4.2) that a ring X with unit which contains more than one member is an integral domain iff $X\backslash\{0\}$ forms a submonoid of the multiplicative monoid X.

In the preceding examples, the rings in (1) are integral domains. The ring $\mathcal{Z}_p$ of integers mod p, $p > 1$, in (2) is an integral domain iff p is a prime. The rings F and E in (3) and (4) are, in general, not integral domains. The ring X in (5) is not an integral domain unless X is a singleton.

By a *division ring* (*quasi-field, skew field,* or *sfield*), we mean an integral domain X in which every nonzero member is invertible in the multiplicative monoid X. Therefore, a nontrivial ring X with unit is a division ring iff $X\backslash\{0\}$ forms a subgroup of the multiplicative semigroup X.

The following theorem is a direct consequence of (4.3) and Exercise 3G.

THEOREM 4.4.   *Every finite integral domain is a division ring.*

Commutative division rings are called *fields*. Hence we have the following corollary of (4.4).

COROLLARY 4.5.   *Every finite commutative integral domain is a field.*

In the preceding examples, the integral domain Z of all integers is not a field since every integer other than ± 1 is not invertible. The integral domains Q, R, C are fields. The ring Z_p of integers mod p, $p > 1$, is a field iff p is a prime.

Now let X denote an arbitrarily given ring. By a *subring* of the ring X, we mean a nonempty subset A of X which is itself a ring with respect to the binary operations defined in X. Therefore, a nonempty subset A of the ring X is a subring of X iff A is a subgroup of the additive group of X and a subsemigroup of the multiplicative semigroup of X. Here, the distributive laws, being valid in the ring X, of course also hold in A. The following lemma is obvious.

LEMMA 4.6.   *A nonempty subset A of a ring X is a subring of X iff $u - v \in A$ and $uv \in A$ hold for all members u and v of A.*

For example, the ring Z of all integers is a subring of the ring Q of all rational numbers, the ring Q is a subring of the ring R of all real numbers, and the ring R is a subring of the ring C of all complex numbers. For any given integer n, the subset nZ of the ring Z which consists of all multiples of the integer n is a subring of Z.

By a *subdomain* of a ring X, we mean a subring A of X which happens to be an integral domain.

For example, the subring Z of all integers is a subdomain of the ring Q of all rational numbers, while the subring nZ is not a subdomain of Z when $n \neq \pm 1$ since it has no unit.

LEMMA 4.7.   *A nontrivial subring A of an integral domain X is a subdomain of X iff A contains the unit of X.*

Proof. Sufficiency.   Assume that A is a subring of X and contains the unit 1 of X. Then it is obvious that A has no divisor of zero and that 1 is a unit of A. Hence A is a subdomain of X.

Necessity.   Assume that A is a nontrivial subdomain of X. Then A has a unit which will be denoted by e. Since 1 is the unit of X, we have

$$ee = e = e1.$$

Since A is nontrivial, we must have $e \neq 0$. Hence it follows from (4.3) that $e = 1$. This proves that A contains the unit 1 of X.‖

By a *subfield* of a ring X, we mean a subring A of X which happens to be a field. Hence, a subfield of a ring X is always a subdomain of X but the converse is not always true.

For example, the subdomain Q of all rational numbers is a subfield of the ring R of all real numbers, while the subdomain Z of all integers is not a subfield of R.

The following lemma is obvious.

LEMMA 4.8. *A subring A of a field X is a subfield of X iff $a^{-1} \epsilon A$ holds for every nonzero member a of A.*

By a *left ideal* of a ring X, we mean a subring A of X which satisfies the condition $xa \epsilon A$ for each $a \epsilon A$ and each $x \epsilon X$. Similarly, a *right ideal* of a ring X is a subring A of X which satisfies the condition $ax \epsilon A$ for every $a \epsilon A$ and every $x \epsilon X$. If a subring A of a ring X is both a left ideal and a right ideal of X, then we say that A is an *ideal* of X.

For examples, the subring nZ of all multiples of an integer n is an ideal of the ring Z of all integers, while Z is not an ideal of the ring Q of all rational numbers.

Every ring X has two obvious ideals, namely X itself and the trivial ideal 0 which consists of only the zero of X. Any ideal of X other than these two obvious ones will be referred to as a *nontrivial proper ideal* of X.

THEOREM 4.9. *Every division ring has no nontrivial proper ideal.*

Proof. Let A be any nontrivial ideal of a division ring X. It suffices to prove $A = X$. Choose a nonzero member a of A. Since X is a division ring, the nonzero member a of X has an inverse $a^{-1} \epsilon X$. Since A is an ideal, we have

$$1 = aa^{-1} \epsilon A.$$

Let x denote an arbitrary member of X. Since A is an ideal and 1 is in A, we have

$$x = 1x \epsilon A.$$

This proves $A = X.\|$

In particular, we have the following corollary of (4.9).

COROLLARY 4.10. *Every field has no nontrivial proper ideal.*

In the proof of (4.9), we have proved the following lemma.

LEMMA 4.11. *If X is a ring with unit and if A is an ideal of X containing the unit of X, then $A = X$.*

By a *homomorphism* of a ring X into a ring Y, we mean a function

$$h : X \rightarrow Y$$

which is a homomorphism of the additive Abelian group X into the additive Abelian group Y and also a homomorphism of the multiplicative semigroup X into the multiplicative semigroup Y. Hence, h is a homomorphism iff it preserves both sum and product, that is to say,

$$h(a + b) = h(a) + h(b)$$
$$h(ab) = h(a)h(b)$$

hold for all members a and b of X.

For example, the inclusion function $i:A \rightarrow X$ from a subring A of a ring X into X is a homomorphism of the ring A into the ring X. This special homomorphism i is called the *inclusion homomorphism* of A into X. In particular, the identity function on a ring X is a homomorphism of X into itself, called the *identity homomorphism*.

THEOREM 4.12.   *If $h:X \rightarrow Y$ is a homomorphism of a ring X into a ring Y, then the image*

$$\text{Im}(h) = h(X)$$

of h is a subring of the ring Y and the kernel

$$\text{Ker}(h) = h^{-1}(0)$$

of h is an ideal of the ring X.

Proof.   According to (3.11) and (2.4), $\text{Im}(h)$ is a subgroup of the additive Abelian group of Y and is also a subsemigroup of the multiplicative semigroup of Y. Hence, $\text{Im}(h)$ is a subring of the ring Y. Similarly, one can prove that $\text{Ker}(h)$ is a subring of the ring X.

It remains to prove that the subring $\text{Ker}(h)$ of X is an ideal. For this purpose, let $a \in \text{Ker}(h)$ and $x \in X$ be arbitrarily given. Then we have

$$h(xa) = h(x)h(a) = h(x)0 = 0.$$

This proves $xa \in \text{Ker}(h)$. Similarly, one can prove $ax \in \text{Ker}(h)$. Therefore, $\text{Ker}(h)$ is an ideal of the ring X.‖

The terms epimorphism, monomorphism, isomorphism, etc., have their obvious meaning for rings and hence their precise definitions are left to the student.

A ring X is said to be of *characteristic* 0 (or *infinity*) iff $m = 0$ is the only integer such that $mx = 0$ holds for all members x of X. Otherwise, the least positive integer m satisfying $mx = 0$ for all $x \in X$ is said to be the *characteristic* of the ring X.

A member x of an additive group X is said to be of *infinite order* iff there exists no positive integer m satisfying $mx = 0$. Otherwise, x is said to be of *finite order* and the least positive integer m satisfying $mx = 0$ is called the *order* of x.

LEMMA 4.13. *Let X be a ring with unit 1. Then X is of characteristic 0 iff 1 is of infinite order in the additive Abelian group of X; otherwise, the characteristic of X is equal to the order of 1.*

Proof. First assume that 1 is of finite order m. Then we have

$$mx = m(1x) = (m1)x = 0x = 0$$

for every $x \in X$. This implies that X is of characteristic m.

Next assume that 1 is of infinite order. Then it is obvious from the definition that X is of characteristic 0. This completes the proof.‖

LEMMA 4.14. *If X is a ring with no divisor of zero, then the orders of all nonzero members of the additive group X are equal.*

Proof. Consider any two nonzero members a and b of X and assume that a is of finite order m. It suffices to prove $mb = 0$. For this purpose, we have

$$a(mb) = mab = (ma)b = 0b = 0.$$

Since X has no divisor of zero and a is different from 0, this implies $mb = 0$.‖

LEMMA 4.15. *If a nontrivial ring X with no divisor of zero is not of characteristic 0, then its characteristic is a prime number.*

Proof. Let m denote the characteristic of X. Since X is nontrivial, there is a nonzero member $x \in X$. According to (4.14) and the definition of characteristic, x is of order m. Let m be represented as the product pq of two positive integers p and q. Then we have

$$(px)(qx) = pqx^2 = mx^2 = 0.$$

Since X has no divisor of zero, we must have $px = 0$ or $qx = 0$. Since x is of order m, it follows that one of the two integers p and q must be m and hence the other must be 1. This implies that m is a prime number.‖

The following theorem is a direct consequence of Lemmas (4.14) and (4.15).

THEOREM 4.16. *A nontrivial ring X with no divisor of zero is of characteristic 0 iff every nonzero member of X is of infinite order; otherwise, the characteristic of X is a prime number p and every nonzero member of X is of order p.*

In Example (5), we saw that every Abelian group can be the additive group of a ring. Now we have shown that simple restrictions imposed on the multiplicative semigroup of a ring imply rather strong restrictions on the additive group.

In the examples, the rings Z, Q, R, and C are of characteristic 0 and the ring Z_p of integers mod p is of characteristic p.

EXERCISES

4A. Prove the following statements:

  (i)   The intersection of any family of subrings of a ring X is a subring of X.

  (ii) The intersection of any family of subdomains of an integral domain X is a subdomain of X.

  (iii) The intersection of any family of subfields of a field X is a subfield of X.

  (iv) The intersection of any family of ideals of a ring X is an ideal of X.

Let S denote a given subset of X. Define the concepts of the *subring*, the *subdomain*, the *subfield*, and the *ideal* of X *generated by S*.

4B. Prove that every ring X with a unit is isomorphic to a subring of the ring $E(X)$ of all endomorphisms of the additive Abelian group X.

4C. Prove that the only endomorphisms of the ring Z of all integers are the trivial endomorphism 0 and the identity endomorphism 1.

4D. Prove that, in an integral domain X of characteristic 0, the additive subgroup of X generated by the unit 1 of X is a subdomain of X isomorphic to the integral domain Z of all integers.

4E. Prove that, in an integral domain X of characteristic $p \geqslant 2$, the additive subgroup of X generated by the unit 1 of X is a subfield of X isomorphic to the field Z_p of all integers mod p.

4F. Prove that, in a field X of characteristic 0, the subfield of X generated by the unit 1 of X is isomorphic to the field Q of all rational numbers.

5. MODULES, VECTOR SPACES, AND ALGEBRAS

In the present section, we will study algebraic structures with a scalar multiplication together with one or two binary operations. These are modules, vector spaces, and algebras.

Let K denote an arbitrarily given ring with a unit 1. This given ring K will be referred to as the *coefficient ring* (or the *ring of scalars*).

By a *module over* K, or a *K-module*, we mean an additive Abelian group X together with a function

$$\mu:K \times X \to X$$

from the Cartesian product $K \times X$ into X which satisfies the following three conditions:

(**M1**) The function is *biadditive;* that is,

$$\mu(\alpha + \beta, x) = \mu(\alpha, x) + \mu(\beta, x),$$
$$\mu(\alpha, x + y) = \mu(\alpha, x) + \mu(\alpha, y)$$

hold for all α, β in K and all x, y in X.

(**M2**) For arbitrary α, β in K and any x in X, we have

$$\mu[\alpha, \mu(\beta, x)] = \mu(\alpha\beta, x).$$

(**M3**) For every $x \in X$, we have

$$\mu(1, x) = x.$$

The function μ is known as the *scalar multiplication* of the module X. For every $\alpha \in K$ and every $x \in X$, the member $\mu(\alpha, x)$ of X will be called the *scalar product* of x by α and will be denoted by αx. In this simplified notation, the conditions (**M1**)–(**M3**) consist of the following four equalities:

$$(\alpha + \beta)x = \alpha x + \beta x,$$
$$\alpha(x + y) = \alpha x + \alpha y,$$
$$\alpha(\beta x) = (\alpha\beta)x,$$
$$1x = x,$$

holding for all members α, β of K and x, y of X. Because of the third formula given above, $\alpha\beta x$ is a well-defined member of the module X.

EXAMPLES OF MODULES

(**1**) Take the coefficient ring K to be the ring Z of all integers. For any given Abelian group X, define a function

$$\mu:Z \times X \to X$$

by taking $\mu(n, x) = nx$ for every integer $n \in Z$ and every member $x \in X$. This function μ satisfies the conditions (**M1**)–(**M3**) and hence makes X a module over Z. Thus every Abelian group can be considered as a module over the ring Z of all integers.

(2) Let X denote any ring with a unit 1 and let K be a subring of X containing 1. Then the function

$$\mu : K \times X \to X$$

defined by $\mu(\alpha, x) = \alpha x$ for every $\alpha \in K$ and every $x \in X$ satisfies Conditions (**M1**)–(**M3**). Thus every ring X with unit 1 is a module over any of its subring K containing 1. In particular, every ring with a unit can be considered as a module over itself.

(3) Let K denote any ring with a unit 1. Consider the set $X = K^S$ of all functions from a set S into the ring K. Then X is an Abelian group with respect to the functional addition defined by

$$(f + g)(s) = f(s) + g(s)$$

for all members f, g of X and every member s of S. Define a function

$$\mu : K \times X \to X$$

by assigning to each member (α, f) of $K \times X$ the function

$$\mu(\alpha, f) = \alpha f : S \to K$$

given by

$$(\alpha f)(s) = \alpha[f(s)]$$

for every member s of S. This function μ satisfies Conditions (**M1**)–(**M3**) and hence makes X a module over K. In particular, if S consists of the first n natural numbers $1, 2, \ldots, n$, then X is the nth Cartesian power K^n of K. Thus, K^n is a module over K.

(4) Let A denote an arbitrarily given Abelian group. Consider the ring $E = E(A)$ of all endomorphisms of A as defined in (§4, Example 4). The identity endomorphism 1 of A is the unit of E. Define a function

$$\mu : E \times A \to A$$

by taking $\mu(h, a) = h(a)$ for every $h \in E$ and every $a \in A$. This function μ satisfies Conditions (**M1**)–(**M3**). Thus every Abelian group can be considered as a module over its ring of all endomorphisms.

Modules over a field F are called *vector spaces* over F.

For example, every field is a vector space over any of its subfields, in particular, over itself. According to Example (**3**), the set F^S of all functions from a set S into a field F is a vector space over F; in particular, the nth Cartesian power F^n of a field F is a vector space over F, called the *standard n-dimensional vector space over F*.

Now let K denote any commutative ring with a unit 1. By an *algebra over* K, we mean a module X over K together with a binary operation in X, called the *multiplication* in X, such that

$$(\alpha u + \beta v)w = \alpha(uw) + \beta(vw),$$
$$w(\alpha u + \beta v) = \alpha(wu) + \beta(wv)$$

hold for all members α, β of K and u, v, w of X. In particular, we have

$$(\alpha u)v = \alpha(uv) = u(\alpha v)$$

for all $\alpha \in K$ and all u, $v \in X$. Thus, αuv is a well-defined member of X.

EXAMPLES OF ALGEBRAS

(**a**) Let X denote any ring with a unit 1, and let K denote a subring of X containing 1 such that every member α of K commutes with every member x of X. In this case, the multiplication in the ring X satisfies the conditions in the definition of an algebra. Hence, X is an algebra over K. In particular, every commutative ring X with a unit 1 is an algebra over every subring K of X containing 1.

(**b**) Let K denote any commutative ring with a unit 1 and let M denote the set of all nonnegative integers. By Example (3), the set $X = K^M$ of all functions $f : M \to K$ is a module over K. Define a multiplication in X by taking the product fg of any two members f, g of X to be the function $fg : M \to K$ given

$$(fg)(n) = \sum_{i=0}^{n} f(i)g(n - i)$$

for every nonnegative integer n. Let $x \in X$ denote the function $x : M \to K$ defined by

$$x(n) = \begin{cases} 1 & (\text{if } n = 1), \\ 0 & (\text{if } n \neq 1). \end{cases}$$

Then every member f of X can be symbolically expressed by a power series

$$f = f(0) + f(1)x + \cdots + f(n)x^n + \cdots.$$

Because of this, X is called the *algebra of all power series with coefficients in K.*

By imposing conditions on the multiplication, we will obtain various types of algebras, namely, *commutative algebras, associative algebras,* and *algebras with unit.* An associative algebra with a unit is said to be a *division algebra* iff every nonzero member is invertible. For example, every commutative division ring X is a division algebra over every subring K of X containing the unit of X.

Let X denote an arbitrarily given module over a ring K with a unit 1. By a *submodule* of X, we mean a nonempty subset A of X which is itself a module over K with respect to the addition and the scalar multiplication of the module X. In other words, a nonempty subset A of X is a submodule of X iff A is a subgroup of the additive Abelian group of X and is *stable* under the scalar multiplication of X. The latter means that $\alpha x \in A$ holds for every $\alpha \in K$ and every $x \in A$.

Submodules of a vector space X are called *subspaces* of X.

EXAMPLES OF SUBMODULES

(**A**) Every subgroup A of any additive Abelian group X is a submodule of X considered as a module over the ring Z of all integers.

(**B**) Every ideal A of a ring X with a unit is a submodule of X considered as a module over itself.

(**C**) Consider the module $X = K^S$ over a ring K in Example (**3**) of modules. Let A denote the subset of X consisting of all functions $f:S \to K$ such that $f(s) = 0$ holds for all except at most a finite number of $s \in S$. Then A is a submodule of X.

Now let X denote an arbitrary algebra over a commutative ring K with a unit 1.

By a *subalgebra* of X, we mean a submodule A of X which is itself an algebra over K with respect to the multiplication of X. In other words, a submodule A of X is a subalgebra of X iff it is *stable* under the multiplication of X; that is, $uv \in A$ holds for every $u \in A$ and every $v \in A$.

For an example of subalgebra, let us consider the algebra $X = K^M$ of all power series with coefficients in a commutative ring K with a unit 1 as defined in Example (**b**) of algebras. Let A denote the subset of X which consists of all functions $f:M \to K$ such that $f(n) = 0$ for all except a finite number of integers $n \in M$. It is easy to verify that A is a subalgebra of X. This subalgebra A of X is called the *polynomial algebra* of the given commutative ring K. Every member f of this algebra over K can be expressed in the form

$$f = a_0 + a_1 x + a_2 x^2 + \cdots + a_n x^n$$

where $x:M \to K$ denotes the function given by

$$x(m) = \begin{cases} 1 & \text{(if } m = 1), \\ 0 & \text{(if } m \neq 1) \end{cases}$$

and $n \in M$, $a_i \in K$ $(i = 0, 1, 2, \ldots, n)$ depend on the member f. Because of this fact, the members of A are called *polynomials* in x with coefficients in the commutative ring K. In case $a_n \neq 0$, the polynomial f is said to be of *degree n*.

By a *left ideal* of an algebra X over K, we mean a subalgebra A of X such that $xa \in A$ holds for every $x \in X$ and every $a \in A$. Similarly, a *right ideal* of an algebra X over K is a subalgebra A of X satisfying $ax \in A$ for every $a \in A$ and every $x \in X$. A subalgebra A of X is said to be an *ideal* of X iff A is both a left ideal and a right ideal of X.

By a *homomorphism* (or *linear mapping*) of a module X over a ring K with a unit 1 into a module Y over the same ring K, we mean a function

$$f:X \rightarrow Y$$

which is a homomorphism of the additive Abelian group of X into the additive Abelian group of Y and preserves the scalar multiplication. In other words, f is a homomorphism of the module X into the module Y iff

$$f(u + v) = f(u) + f(v),$$
$$f(\alpha u) = \alpha f(u)$$

hold for all $\alpha \in K$ and all u, $v \in X$.

For example, the inclusion function $i:A \rightarrow X$ of a submodule A of any module X into X is a homomorphism of the module A into the module X, called the *inclusion homomorphism*. In particular, the identity function on a module X is a homomorphism of the module X into itself, called the *identity homomorphism*.

THEOREM 5.1. *If $h:X \rightarrow Y$ is any homomorphism of a module X over K into a module Y over K, then the image*

$$\mathrm{Im}(h) = h(X)$$

of h is a submodule of the module Y and the kernel

$$\mathrm{Ker}(h) = h^{-1}(0)$$

of h is a submodule of the module X.

Proof. Since h is by definition a homomorphism of the additive Abelian group X into the additive Abelian group Y, it follows from (3.11) that $\mathrm{Im}(h)$ and $\mathrm{Ker}(h)$ are subgroups. It remains to prove that both are stable under the scalar multiplication.

For this purpose, let y denote an arbitrary member of $\mathrm{Im}(h)$. By definition, there exists an $x \in X$ with $h(x) = y$. Then we have

$$\alpha y = \alpha h(x) = h(\alpha x) \in \mathrm{Im}(h)$$

for every $\alpha \in K$. This proves that $\mathrm{Im}(h)$ is a submodule of Y.

On the other hand, let x denote any member of Ker(h). By definition, we have $h(x) = 0$. Then we have

$$h(\alpha x) = \alpha h(x) = 0$$

for every $\alpha \in K$. This implies $\alpha x \in$ Ker(h) for every $\alpha \in K$. Hence Ker(h) is a submodule of X.‖

The terms *epimorphism, monomorphism, isomorphism,* etc., have their obvious meaning for modules, and hence their precise definitions are left to the student.

Now let K denote a commutative ring with unit 1. By a *homomorphism* of an algebra X over K into an algebra Y over K, we mean a homomorphism

$$h : X \to Y$$

of the module X into the module Y which preserves products. The latter means that

$$h(uv) = h(u)h(v)$$

holds for all members u and v of X.

For example, the inclusion function $i : A \to X$ of a subalgebra A of any algebra X into X is a homomorphism of the algebra A into the algebra X, called the *inclusion homomorphism*. In particular, the identity function on an algebra X is a homomorphism called the *identity homomorphism*.

The following theorem can be proved as in (4.12).

THEOREM 5.2. *If $h : X \to Y$ is a homomorphism of an algebra X over K into an algebra Y over K, then the image*

$$\mathrm{Im}(h) = h(X)$$

of h is a subalgebra of the algebra Y and the kernel

$$\mathrm{Ker}(h) = h^{-1}(0)$$

of h is an ideal of the algebra X.

The terms *epimorphism, monomorphism, isomorphism,* etc. have the obvious meaning for algebras, and hence their precise definitions are left to the student.

EXERCISES

5A. The modules defined in the text are usually called *left modules*. Define a *right module* X over a ring K with unit 1 by means of a *right scalar multiplication* $x\alpha$ for each $x \in X$ and each $\alpha \in K$ satisfying

$$x(\alpha + \beta) = x\alpha + x\beta,$$
$$(x + y)\alpha = x\alpha + y\alpha,$$
$$(x\alpha)\beta = x(\alpha\beta),$$
$$x1 = x$$

for all members α, β of K and x, y of X. Prove that, for a commutative ring K, the notions of left module and right module over K essentially coincide.

5B. Prove that, for an arbitrary member x of any given module X over K, the assignment $\alpha \rightarrow \alpha x$ defines a homomorphism

$$h_x : K \rightarrow X$$

of the additive Abelian group of K into the additive Abelian group of X. Hence

$$0x = 0, \qquad (\alpha - \beta)x = \alpha x - \beta x, \qquad n(\alpha x) = (n\alpha)x$$

hold for all members α, β of K and every integer n. By means of these, prove that $px = 0$ holds for all members x of X if K is of characteristic p.

5C. Prove that a nonempty subset A of a module X over K is a submodule of X iff $u + v \in A$ and $\alpha u \in A$ hold for all members u, v of A and α of K.

5D. Let J denote an ideal of a ring K with unit 1 and let x denote a given member of a module X over K. Prove that the subset

$$A = \{\alpha x \mid \alpha \in J\}$$

of X is a submodule of X.

5E. Let $h : X \rightarrow Y$ denote any homomorphism of a module X into a module Y. Prove that the image $h(A)$ of any submodule A of X is a submodule of Y and the inverse image $h^{-1}(B)$ of any submodule B of Y is a submodule of X.

Chapter IV: GEOMETRIES

In the first two sections of the present chapter, we will define the spaces which geometries study, namely, the Euclidean spaces and the projective spaces. In the last three sections, we will introduce three geometries, partially following Klein's Erlangen Program.

1. EUCLIDEAN SPACES

Let n denote an arbitrarily given positive integer. Consider the Cartesian power

$$R^n$$

of the real line R as defined in (I, §7). Let

$$K = \{1, 2, \ldots, n\}$$

denote the set of the first n positive integers. Then the members of R^n are, by definition, the functions

$$x : K \to R.$$

For each $i \in K$, the real number

$$x_i = x(i)$$

will be called the ith *coordinate* of x. Traditionally, the member $x : K \to R$ of R^n is denoted by the ordered n-tuple

$$x = (x_1, x_2, \ldots, x_n)$$

of real numbers. Hereafter, R^n will be referred to as the *n-dimensional Euclidean space* and the members of R^n will be called *points* of R^n.

Consider the functional addition in R^n. This is precisely defined as follows: For any two points x and y in R^n considered as functions from K into R, their *sum* $x + y$ is a function

$$x + y : K \to R$$

defined by

$$(x + y)(i) = x(i) + y(i)$$

126

for every $i \in K$. In the traditional notation of points of R^n as n-tuples of real numbers, we have

$$x + y = (x_1 + y_1, x_2 + y_2, \ldots, x_n + y_n).$$

Because of this, the functional addition in R^n is often called the *coordinatewise addition*. Hereafter, this will be referred to simply as the *addition* in R^n.

Since the set R of all real numbers is an Abelian group with respect to addition, it can be easily verified that the addition in R^n makes R^n an Abelian group. The neutral element of this Abelian group R^n is the point

$$O = (0, 0, \ldots, 0)$$

of which the ith coordinate is the real number 0 for every $i \in K$. This special point O of R^n will be referred to as the *origin* of R^n. On the other hand, the additive inverse of any point

$$x = (x_1, x_2, \ldots, x_n)$$

of R^n is the point

$$-x = (-x_1, -x_2, \ldots, -x_n).$$

Define a function

$$\mu : R \times R^n \to R^n$$

by setting

$$\mu(\lambda, x) = \lambda x = (\lambda x_1, \lambda x_2, \ldots, \lambda x_n)$$

for every real number $\lambda \in R$ and every point $x = (x_1, x_2, \ldots, x_n)$ of R^n. One can easily verify that μ satisfies the three conditions (**M1**)–(**M3**) in (III, §5). Thus the Abelian group R^n becomes a module over R with μ as scalar multiplication. Since the ring R of all real numbers is a field, R^n is a vector space over the field R. Because of this fact, the points of R^n are often called *n-vectors*.

For an arbitrary integer $j \in K$, let us consider the subset X_j of R^n which consists of all points $x \in R^n$ satisfying $x(i) = 0$ for every $i \neq j$ in K. This subset X_j of R^n will be called the jth *coordinate axis* of R^n. In particular, the point $u_j \in X_j$ with $u_j(j) = 1$ will be referred to as the *unit point of the jth axis X_j* or the jth *unit point of R^n*. Every point of R^n can be written as a linear combination of these n unit points $u_1, u_2, \ldots, u_n$; in fact, we have

$$x = (x_1, x_2, \ldots, x_n) = \sum_{j=1}^{n} x_j u_j$$

holds for every point x of R^n. On the other hand, for an arbitrarily given point $x = (x_1, x_2, \ldots, x_n)$ of R^n, it follows immediately from the definitions that

$$x = (x_1, x_2, \ldots, x_n) = \sum_{j=1}^{n} a_j u_j$$

implies $a_j = x_j$ for every $j = 1, 2, \ldots, n$. Because of this, the set

$$B = \{u_1, u_2, \ldots, u_n\}$$

of the n unit points of R^n will be called the *fundamental basis* of R^n.

Consider the Cartesian product $R^n \times R^n$ and define a function

$$\pi : R^n \times R^n \to R$$

by setting

$$\pi(x, y) = \sum_{i=1}^{n} x_i y_i$$

for arbitrary points $x = (x_1, x_2, \ldots, x_n)$ and $y = (y_1, y_2, \ldots, y_n)$ of R^n. The real number $\pi(x, y)$ will be denoted by

$$x \cdot y$$

and will be referred to as the *inner product* of the points x and y of R^n. The function π will be called the *inner multiplication* of R^n.

PROPOSITION 1.1.   *The inner multiplication π of R^n is commutative; that is,*

$$x \cdot y = y \cdot x$$

holds for any two points x and y of R^n.

Proof.   Let $x = (x_1, x_2, \ldots, x_n)$ and $y = (y_1, y_2, \ldots, y_n)$ denote any two points of R^n. Then, by definition, we have

$$x \cdot y = \sum_{i=1}^{n} x_i y_i = \sum_{i=1}^{n} y_i x_i = y \cdot x$$

since the multiplication of real numbers is commutative. This proves (1.1).‖

PROPOSITION 1.2.   *The inner multiplication π of R^n is bilinear; that is, for any three points a, b, x of R^n and any two real numbers α and β, we have*

(i) $(\alpha a + \beta b) \cdot x = \alpha(a \cdot x) + \beta(b \cdot x)$
(ii) $x \cdot (\alpha a + \beta b) = \alpha(x \cdot \alpha) + \beta(x \cdot b).$

Proof. Let $a = (a_1, a_2, \ldots, a_n)$, $b = (b_1, b_2, \ldots, b_n)$, and $x = (x_1, x_2, \ldots, x_n)$. Then we have

$$\alpha a + \beta b = (\alpha a_1 + \beta b_1, \alpha a_2 + \beta b_2, \ldots, \alpha a_n + \beta b_n).$$

Then, by definition, we have

$$(\alpha a + \beta b) \cdot x = \sum_{i=1}^{n} (\alpha a_i + \beta b_i) x_i$$

$$= \alpha \sum_{i=1}^{n} a_i x_i + \beta \sum_{i=1}^{n} b_i x_i$$

$$= \alpha(a \cdot x) + \beta(b \cdot x).$$

This proves (**i**). As for (**ii**), we have

$$x \cdot (\alpha a + \beta b) = (\alpha a + \beta b) \cdot x$$
$$= \alpha(a \cdot x) + \beta(b \cdot x)$$
$$= \alpha(x \cdot a) + \beta(x \cdot b)$$

because of (1.1) and (**i**). This completes the proof of (1.2).‖

In particular, we have

$$x \cdot x = \sum_{i=1}^{n} x_i^2$$

for any point $x = (x_1, x_2, \ldots, x_n)$ of R^n. As the sum of n squares, this inner product $x \cdot x$ is nonnegative and hence the nonnegative square root $\sqrt{(x \cdot x)}$ is well-defined. Thus we may define a function

$$\rho : R^n \to R$$

by setting

$$\rho(x) = \sqrt{(x \cdot x)}$$

for every point x of R^n. The nonnegative real number $\rho(x)$ will be denoted by

$$\| x \|$$

and will be called the *norm* of the point x. The function ρ will be referred to as the *norm function* of R^n.

PROPOSITION 1.3. *For an arbitrary point* $x = (x_1, x_2, \ldots, x_n)$ *of* R^n, $\| x \| = 0$ *holds iff* x *is the origin* O *of* R^n.

Proof. Sufficiency. Assume $x = 0$. Then we have $x_i = 0$ for every $i = 1, 2, \ldots, n$ and hence

$$\| x \| = \sqrt{\sum_{i=1}^{n} x_i^2} = 0.$$

Necessity.   Assume $\| x \| = 0$. Then we have

$$\sum_{i=1}^{n} x_i^2 = \| x \|^2 = 0.$$

Since $x_i^2 \geqslant 0$ holds for every i, this implies $x_i^2 = 0$ and hence $x_i = 0$ for every i. This proves $x = 0.\|$

PROPOSITION 1.4.   *For every real number* $\lambda \in R$ *and every point* $x \in R^n$, *we have*

$$\| \lambda x \| = | \lambda | \cdot \| x \|,$$

where $| \lambda |$ *denotes the absolute value of the real number* λ.

Proof.   Let $x = (x_1, x_2, \ldots, x_n)$. Then we have $\lambda x = (\lambda x_1, \lambda x_2, \ldots, \lambda x_n)$ and hence

$$\| \lambda x \| = \sqrt{\sum_{i=1}^{n} (\lambda x_i)^2} = | \lambda | \sqrt{\sum_{i=1}^{n} x_i^2} = | \lambda | \cdot \| x \|.$$

This proves (1.4).$\|$

PROPOSITION 1.5.   (SCHWARZ INEQUALITY).   *For any two points* x *and* y *of* R^n, *we have*

$$| x \cdot y | \leqslant \| x \| \cdot \| y \|.$$

Proof.   Let $x = (x_1, x_2, \ldots, x_n)$ and $y = (y_1, y_2, \ldots, y_n)$. Define a function

$$f : R^2 \to R$$

by taking

$$f(\alpha, \beta) = \| \alpha x + \beta y \|^2 = \sum_{i=1}^{n} (\alpha x_i + \beta y_i)^2$$
$$= \alpha^2 \| x \|^2 + 2\alpha\beta(x \cdot y) + \beta^2 \| y \|^2$$

for every $(\alpha, \beta) \in R^2$. It follows that

$$f(\alpha, \beta) \geqslant 0$$

holds for every $(\alpha, \beta) \in R^2$. In particular, let $\alpha = -(x \cdot y)$ and $\beta = \| x \|^2$. Then we obtain

$$0 \leqslant f(-x \cdot y, \| x \|^2) = \| x \|^2 [\| x \|^2 \| y \|^2 - (x \cdot y)^2].$$

If $x = 0$, then we have $x_i = 0$ for every $i = 1, 2, \ldots, n$. This implies $\| x \| = 0$ and $x \cdot y = 0$. Hence, in this case, the Schwarz inequality is trivial.

If $x \neq 0$, then we have $\| x \| > 0$ by (1.3). This implies

$$\| x \|^2 \| y \|^2 - (x \cdot y)^2 \geqslant 0$$

and, therefore, the Schwarz inequality also holds in this case.$\|$

PROPOSITION 1.6. *For any two points x and y of R^n with $x \neq 0$,*

$$| x \cdot y | = \| x \| \cdot \| y \|$$

holds iff there exists a real number λ satisfying

$$y = \lambda x.$$

Proof. Let $x = (x_1, x_2, \ldots, x_n)$ and $y = (y_1, y_2, \ldots, y_n)$.

Sufficiency. Assume that $y = \lambda x$. Then it follows from (1.2) and (1.4) that we have

$$x \cdot y = \lambda(x \cdot x) = \lambda \| x \|^2, \qquad \| y \| = | \lambda | \cdot \| x \|.$$

This implies

$$| x \cdot y | = | \lambda | \cdot \| x \|^2 = \| x \| \cdot \| y \|.$$

Necessity. Assume that $| x \cdot y | = \| x \| \cdot \| y \|$. This implies

$$\| x \|^2 \| y \|^2 - (x \cdot y)^2 = \left(\sum_{i=1}^{n} x_i^2 \right) \left(\sum_{i=1}^{n} y_i^2 \right) - \left(\sum_{i=1}^{n} x_i y_i \right)^2$$

$$= \sum_{i=1}^{n} x_i^2 y_i^2 + \sum_{i \neq j}^{n} x_i^2 y_j^2 - \sum_{i=1}^{n} x_i^2 y_i^2 - 2 \sum_{i<j}^{n} x_i x_j y_i y_j$$

$$= \sum_{i \neq j}^{n} x_i^2 y_j^2 - 2 \sum_{i<j}^{n} x_i x_j y_i y_j$$

$$= \sum_{i<j}^{n} (x_i y_j - x_j y_i)^2.$$

It follows that we have

$$x_i y_j - x_j y_i = 0$$

for every pair of distinct integers i and j in $K = \{1, 2, \ldots, n\}$. Since $x \neq 0$, there exists an integer $j \in K$ with $x_j \neq 0$. Let

$$\lambda = y_j / x_j.$$

Then we obtain

$$y_i = x_i y_j / x_j = \lambda x_i$$

for every $i \in K$. This proves $y = \lambda x.\|$

PROPOSITION 1.7. (TRIANGLE INEQUALITY). *For any two points x and y of R^n, we have*

$$\| x + y \| \leqslant \| x \| + \| y \|.$$

Proof. Let $x = (x_1, x_2, \ldots, x_n)$ and $y = (y_1, y_2, \ldots, y_n)$. Then we have

$$\| x + y \|^2 = \sum_{i=1}^{n} (x_i + y_i)^2 = \| x \|^2 + \| y \|^2 + 2(x \cdot y),$$
$$(\| x \| + \| y \|)^2 = \| x \|^2 + \| y \|^2 + 2(\| x \| \cdot \| y \|).$$

According to the Schwarz inequality, we have

$$x \cdot y \leqslant | x \cdot y | \leqslant \| x \| \cdot \| y \|.$$

This implies

$$\| x + y \|^2 \leqslant (\| x \| + \| y \|)^2$$

and proves (1.7).∥

PROPOSITION 1.8.   *For any two points x and y of R^n with $x \neq 0$,*

$$\| x + y \| = \| x \| + \| y \|$$

holds iff there exists a nonnegative real number λ satisfying

$$y = \lambda x.$$

Proof. Let $x = (x_1, x_2, \ldots, x_n)$ and $y = (y_1, y_2, \ldots, y_n)$.

Sufficiency. Assume $y = \lambda x$ with $\lambda \geqslant 0$. Then we have $x + y = (1 + \lambda)x$. This implies

$$\| x + y \| = \| (1 + \lambda)x \| = (1 + \lambda) \| x \|$$
$$= \| x \| + \lambda \| x \| = \| x \| + \| y \|.$$

Necessity. Assume $\| x + y \| = \| x \| + \| y \|$. As in the proof of (1.7), we have

$$\| x + y \|^2 = \| x \|^2 + \| y \|^2 + 2(x \cdot y),$$
$$(\| x \| + \| y \|)^2 = \| x \|^2 + \| y \|^2 + 2(\| x \| \cdot \| y \|).$$

Therefore, $\| x + y \| = \| x \| + \| y \|$ implies

$$| x \cdot y | = \| x \| \cdot \| y \|.$$

Then it follows from (1.6) that there exists a real number λ satisfying

$$y = \lambda x.$$

It remains to prove $\lambda \geqslant 0$. For this purpose, let us consider

$$\| x + y \| = \| (1 + \lambda)x \| = | 1 + \lambda | \cdot \| x \|,$$
$$\| x \| + \| y \| = \| x \| + | \lambda | \cdot \| y \| = (1 + | \lambda |) \| x \|.$$

Since $x \neq 0$, we have $\| x \| > 0$ according to (1.3). Therefore, $\| x + y \| = \| x \| + \| y \|$ implies

$$| 1 + \lambda | = 1 + | \lambda |.$$

This implies $\lambda \geqslant 0$ and completes the proof of (1.8).∥

Now let us define a function

$$d : R^n \times R^n \to R$$

by setting

$$d(x, y) = \| y - x \|$$

for arbitrary points x and y of R^n. The nonnegative real number $d(x, y)$ will be called the *distance from x to y*. The function d will be referred to as the *Euclidean metric* in R^n.

The following proposition is a direct consequence of (1.3).

PROPOSITION 1.9. *For arbitrary points x and y of R^n, $d(x, y) = 0$ holds iff $x = y$.*

The following proposition is a direct consequence of (1.4) with $\lambda = -1$.

PROPOSITION 1.10. *For any two points x and y of R^n, we have*

$$d(x, y) = d(y, x).$$

Because of (1.10), $d(x, y)$ is often called the *distance between the points x and y*.

PROPOSITION 1.11 (TRIANGLE INEQUALITY). *For any three points x, y, z of R^n, we have*

$$d(x, y) + d(y, z) \geqslant d(x, z).$$

Proof. Because of the equality

$$z - x = (y - x) + (z - y),$$

it follows from (1.7) that we have

$$d(x, z) = \| z - x \| \leqslant \| y - x \| + \| z - y \| = d(x, y) + d(y, z).$$

This proves (1.11).∥

PROPOSITION 1.12. *For any three points x, y, z of R^n, we have*

$$| d(x, y) - d(y, z) | \leqslant d(x, z).$$

Proof. Applying (1.11) to the points x, z, y of R^n, we obtain

$$d(x, y) \leqslant d(x, z) + d(z, y) = d(x, z) + d(y, z).$$

This implies

$$d(x, y) - d(y, z) \leqslant d(x, z).$$

On the other hand, if we apply (1.11) to the points y, x, z of R^n, we get

$$d(y, z) \leqslant d(y, x) + d(x, z) = d(x, y) + d(x, z).$$

This implies

$$-d(x, z) \leqslant d(x, y) - d(y, z).$$

Combining these two inequalities, we obtain

$$| d(x, y) - d(y, z) | \leqslant d(x, z).$$

This proves (1.12).‖

PROPOSITION 1.13.   *For any three points* x, y, z *of* R^n *with* $x \neq y$, *we have the following assertions:*

(i) $d(x, y) = d(x, z) + d(y, z)$ *holds iff there exists a real number* λ *satisfying*

$$0 \leqslant \lambda \leqslant 1, \qquad z = (1 - \lambda)x + \lambda y.$$

(ii) $d(x, y) = d(x, z) - d(y, z)$ *holds iff there exists a real number* λ *satisfying*

$$\lambda \geqslant 1, \qquad z = (1 - \lambda)x + \lambda y.$$

(iii) $d(x, y) = d(y, z) - d(x, z)$ *holds iff there exists a real number* λ *satisfying*

$$\lambda \leqslant 0, \qquad z = (1 - \lambda)x + \lambda y.$$

Proof of (i).   *Sufficiency.*   Assume $z = (1 - \lambda)x + \lambda y$ with $0 \leqslant \lambda \leqslant 1$. Then we have

$$z - x = \lambda(y - x), \qquad z - y = (1 - \lambda)(x - y).$$

Thus we obtain

$$d(x, z) = \lambda \| y - x \| = \lambda d(x, y),$$
$$d(y, z) = (1 - \lambda) \| y - x \| = (1 - \lambda)d(x, y)$$

and hence

$$d(x, z) + d(y, z) = \lambda d(x, y) + (1 - \lambda)d(x, y) = d(x, y).$$

Necessity.   Assume that $d(x, y) = d(x, z) + d(y, z)$. Because of

$$(z - x) + (y - z) = y - x,$$

we obtain

$$\| (z - x) + (y - z) \| = \| y - x \| = d(x, y)$$
$$= d(x, z) + d(y, z) = \| z - x \| + \| y - z \|.$$

In view of $x \neq y$, we must have either $z \neq x$ or $z \neq y$. Without loss of generality, we may assume $z \neq x$ and hence $z - x \neq 0$. According to (1.8), there exists a nonnegative real number μ satisfying

$$y - z = \mu(z - x).$$

Solving for z, we obtain

$$z = \frac{\mu}{1 + \mu} x + \frac{1}{1 + \mu} y.$$

Let $\lambda = (1 + \mu)^{-1}$. Then we have $0 \leqslant \lambda \leqslant 1$ and

$$z = (1 - \lambda)x + \lambda y.$$

This completes the proof of (**i**).$\|$

The proofs of (**ii**) and (**iii**) are similar to that of (**i**) and hence are left to the student.

EXERCISES

1A. Let a and b denote any two distinct points of R^n. The subset

$$L(a, b) = \{(1 - \lambda)a + \lambda b \mid \lambda \in R\}$$

of R^n is called the *(straight) line determined by the points a and b in R^n* and the subset

$$\overline{ab} = \{(1 - \lambda)a + \lambda b \mid \lambda \in I = [0, 1]\}$$

of $L(a, b)$ is called the *segment of $L(a, b)$ between the points a and b.* Prove that

$$L(x, y) = L(a, b)$$

holds for any two distinct points x and y on $L(a, b)$. A subset L of R^n is said to be a *(straight) line* iff there exist two distinct points a and b of L satisfying

$$L = L(a, b).$$

1B. Let L denote an arbitrary line in R_n and (a, b) any ordered pair of distinct points of L. By Ex. 1A, prove that $L = L(a, b)$. For each $i = 1, 2, \ldots, n$, let

$$w_i = (b_i - a_i)/\| b - a \|.$$

Then the point

$$w = w(\overline{ab}) = (w_1, w_2, \ldots, w_n)$$

of R^n is called the *direction of the segment ab.* Since $\| w \| = 1$, w is often called the *unit point*, or *unit vector*, of R^n. Prove that

$$w(\overline{ba}) = -w(\overline{ab}).$$

Consider any other ordered pair (x, y) of distinct points of L. Since $L = L(ab)$, there exist real numbers ξ and η satisfying $x = (1 - \xi)a + \xi b$ and $y = (1 - \eta)a + \eta b$. Prove that

$$w(\overline{xy}) = \text{sgn}(\eta - \xi)w(\overline{ab}),$$

where $\text{sgn}: R \to R$ denotes the function defined by

$$\text{sgn}(\lambda) = \begin{cases} 1 & (\text{if } \lambda > 0), \\ 0 & (\text{if } \lambda = 0), \\ -1 & (\text{if } \lambda < 0). \end{cases}$$

Hence, for all possible choices of the ordered pair (x, y) of distinct points of L, we will get only two directions, namely

$$\pm w = \pm w(\overline{ab}).$$

These two directions $\pm w$ will be referred to as the *two directions of the line L*, each is said to be the *opposite* of the other. By a *directed line*, we mean a line L together with one of its two directions.

1C. Three points a, b, c of R^n are said to be *collinear* iff there exists a line L in R^n which contains each of them; otherwise, a, b, c are said to be *noncollinear*. By a *triangle* in R^n, we mean three noncollinear points a, b, c of R^n, called *vertices*, together with the three segments $\overline{ab}$, $\overline{ac}$, $\overline{bc}$, called *sides*. The distances $d(a, b)$, $d(a, c)$, $d(b, c)$ are called the *lengths* of the sides $\overline{ab}$, $\overline{ac}$, $\overline{bc}$. Prove that

$$| d(a, b) - d(a, c) | < d(b, c) < d(a, b) + d(a, c).$$

1D. Two lines in R^n are said to be *parallel* iff they can be directed by the same direction. Prove the *Euclidean postulate of parallelism* which states that, for any given line L in R^n and an arbitrary point $a \in R^n$, there exists a unique line M in R^n which contains the point a and is parallel to L. Furthermore, prove that this unique line M is given by

$$M = \{a + \lambda w \in R^n \mid \lambda \in R\}$$

in case w is a direction of the line L.

1E. Two lines in R^n with directions $\pm u$ and $\pm v$ are said to be *perpendicular* iff $u \cdot v = 0$. Consider a triangle $\triangle$ in R^n with vertices a, b, and c. Prove the *Pythagorean theorem* which states that

$$[d(a, b)]^2 + [d(a, c)]^2 = [d(b, c)]^2$$

holds iff the two lines $L(a, b)$ and $L(a, c)$ are perpendicular.

1F. Let us consider in R^n any point a and any line L. The union of all lines in R^n containing the point a and perpendicular to the line L is a subset $\pi(a, L)$ of R^n called the *hyperplane in R^n containing a and perpendicular to L*. A subset π of R^n is said to be a *hyperplane* iff there exists a point $a \in \pi$ and a line L in R^n with $\pi = \pi(a, L)$. Let w denote a direction of the line L. Prove that

$$\pi(a, L) = \{x \in R^n \mid w \cdot (x - a) = 0\}.$$

Let $r = w \cdot a$. It follows that every hyperplane π in R^n consists of all points $x \in R^n$ satisfying a linear equation of the form

$$w \cdot x = r.$$

Conversely, for every point $b \neq 0$ of R^n and every $c \in R$, prove that the subset

$$\{x \in R^n \mid b \cdot x = c\}$$

of R^n is a hyperplane. In case $n = 2$, prove that a subset of R^2 is a hyperplane iff it is a line.

2. PROJECTIVE SPACES

For an arbitrary positive integer n, let us consider the $(n + 1)$-dimensional Euclidean space R^{n+1} as defined in the preceding section. The points of R^{n+1} are the $(n + 1)$-tuples

$$x = (x_1, \ldots, x_n, x_{n+1})$$

of real numbers. If we delete from R^{n+1} the origin $O = (0, \ldots, 0, 0)$ of R^{n+1}, we obtain a subset

$$W = R^{n+1} \setminus \{O\}.$$

Introduce a relation $\sim$ in the set W as follows. Let

$$x = (x_1, \ldots, x_n, x_{n+1}), \qquad y = (y_1, \ldots, y_n, y_{n+1})$$

denote any two points of W. Then we define

$$x \sim y$$

iff there exists a nonzero real number λ such that $y = \lambda x$ holds; that is,

$$y_i = \lambda x_i$$

holds for every $i = 1, \ldots, n, n + 1$.

LEMMA 2.1. *The relation $\sim$ in the set $W = R^{n+1} \setminus \{O\}$ is an equivalence relation.*

Proof. We have to verify that the relation $\sim$ in W is reflexive, symmetric, and transitive.

To prove that $\sim$ is reflexive, let x denote an arbitrary point of W. Since

$$x = \lambda x$$

holds with $\lambda = 1$, we obtain $x \sim x$ and hence $\sim$ is reflexive.

To prove that $\sim$ is symmetric, let x and y denote any two points of W satisfying $x \sim y$. By definition, this implies the existence of a nonzero real number λ such that

$$y = \lambda x$$

holds. Because $\lambda \neq 0$, it follows that

$$x = \lambda^{-1} y.$$

Since λ^{-1} is a nonzero real number, this implies that $y \sim x$ and hence $\sim$ is symmetric.

To prove that $\sim$ is transitive, let x, y, and z denote any three points of W satisfying $x \sim y$ and $y \sim z$. By definition, there exist two nonzero real numbers λ and μ satisfying

$$y = \lambda x, \qquad z = \mu y.$$

It follows that we have

$$z = \mu y = \mu(\lambda x) = (\mu\lambda)x.$$

Since $\mu\lambda$ is a nonzero real number, this implies that $x \sim z$ and hence $\sim$ is transitive.$\|$

The equivalence relation $\sim$ in W divides W into disjoint nonempty equivalence classes. Let

$$P^n = W/\sim$$

denote the quotient set of all equivalence classes in W. This set P^n is called the *n-dimensional (real) projective space*. The members of P^n are called the points of P^n. Thus the points of the n-dimensional projective space P^n are the equivalence classes in the set

$$W = R^{n+1} \backslash \{0\}.$$

In particular, P^1 is called the *(real) projective line* and P^2 is called the *(real) projective plane*.

Consider the natural projection

$$\pi : W \to P^n$$

from the set W onto the n-dimensional projective space P^n. For every point $x \in W$, the image $\pi(x) \in P^n$ is the equivalence class in W which contains the point x. Hence, for any two points x and y of W,

$$\pi(x) = \pi(y)$$

holds iff $x \sim y$ holds. For any point $p \in P^n$, the inverse image

$$\pi^{-1}(p) \subset W \subset R^{n+1}$$

is an equivalence class of $\sim$ in W. From the definition of the equivalence relation $\sim$, it is clear that $\pi^{-1}(p)$ is a (straight) line in R^{n+1} passing through the origin O and with the origin O deleted. Because of this, P^n may be considered as the set of all (straight) lines in R^{n+1} passing through the origin O.

Let p denote an arbitrarily given point of P^n. Any point

$$x = (x_1, \ldots, x_n, x_{n+1})$$

of $W = R^{n+1} \setminus \{O\}$ with $\pi(x) = p$ is said to be a set of *homogeneous coordinates* of the point p. Thus any two points

$$x = (x_1, \ldots, x_n, x_{n+1}), \qquad y = (y_1, \ldots, y_n, y_{n+1})$$

of W are homogeneous coordinates of the same point p of P^n iff there exists a nonzero real number λ satisfying

$$y = \lambda x.$$

Now let $a = (a_1, \ldots, a_n, a_{n+1})$ denote an arbitrarily given point of W. For any point $x = (x_1, \ldots, x_n, x_{n+1})$ of W, the inner product

$$a \cdot x = \sum_{i=1}^{n+1} a_i x_i$$

in R^{n+1} is a well-defined real number. Let p denote any point of P^n. By

$$a \cdot p = 0,$$

we mean that, for any set $x = (x_1, \ldots, x_n, x_{n+1})$ of homogeneous coordinates of the point p, we have

$$a \cdot x = 0.$$

LEMMA 2.2. $a \cdot p = 0$ *holds iff there exists a set* $x = (x_1, \ldots, x_n, x_{n+1})$ *of homogeneous coordinates of p such that $a \cdot x = 0$ is satisfied.*

Proof. Since the necessity of the condition is obvious, it remains to prove the sufficiency. For this purpose, assume the existence of a set $x = (x_1, \ldots, x_n, x_{n+1})$ of homogeneous coordinates of the given point $p \in P^n$ satisfying

$$a \cdot x = \sum_{i=1}^{n+1} a_i x_i = 0.$$

To prove $a \cdot p = 0$, let $y = (y_1, \ldots, y_n, y_{n+1})$ denote any set of homogeneous coordinates of p. Then there exists a nonzero real number λ satisfying $y = \lambda x$; that is,

$$y_i = \lambda x_i$$

holds for every $i = 1, \ldots, n, n + 1$. Hence we obtain

$$a \cdot y = a \cdot \lambda x = \lambda(a \cdot x) = 0.$$

This implies $a \cdot p = 0$ and proves (2.2). ‖

For any point $a \in W$, the subset

$$H(a) = \{ p \in P^n \mid a \cdot p = 0 \}$$

of P^n will be called the (*projective*) *hyperplane of P^n determined by the point a.* Often, $H(a)$ is called the *hyperplane of P^n determined by the homogeneous linear equation*

$$a \cdot x = \sum_{i=1}^{n+1} a_i x_i = 0.$$

This homogeneous linear equation is said to be the *equation* of $H(a)$ with $a = (a_1, \ldots, a_n, a_{n+1})$ as *coefficients*.

In particular, the jth unit point u_j, $1 \leqslant j \leqslant n + 1$, of the Euclidean space R^{n+1} determines a hyperplane $H(u_j)$ with equation

$$x_j = 0.$$

This hyperplane $H(u_j)$ will be called the jth *coordinate hyperplane* of P^n.

Now let us consider the function

$$\kappa : R^n \longrightarrow P^n$$

defined by setting

$$\kappa(x_1, \ldots, x_n) = \pi(x_1, \ldots, x_n, 1)$$

for every point $(x_1, \ldots, x_n)$ of R^n, where π denotes the natural projection

$$\pi : W \longrightarrow P^n.$$

LEMMA 2.3.   *The function $\kappa : R^n \longrightarrow P^n$ is injective and its image is the complement of the $(n + 1)$th coordinate hyperplane $H(u_{n+1})$ in P^n; in symbols,*

$$\kappa(R^n) = P^n \backslash H(u_{n+1}).$$

Proof.   To prove that κ is injective, let $x = (x_1, \ldots, x_n)$ and $y = (y_1, \ldots, y_n)$ denote any two points of R^n with $\kappa(x) = \kappa(y)$. Then we obtain

$$\pi(x_1, \ldots, x_n, 1) = \kappa(x) = \kappa(y) = \pi(y_1, \ldots, y_n, 1).$$

This implies the existence of a nonzero real number λ satisfying

$$(y_1, \ldots, y_n, 1) = \lambda(x_1, \ldots, x_n, 1).$$

Equating the last coordinates, we obtain $1 = \lambda$ and hence $y = x$. This proves that κ is injective.

To determine the image $\kappa(R^n)$, let $x = (x_1, \ldots, x_n)$ denote any point of R^n. By the definition of the hyperplane $H(u_{n+1})$, it is obvious that the point

$$\kappa(x) = \pi(x_1, \ldots, x_n, 1)$$

of P^n is not in $H(u_{n+1})$. Hence we obtain

$$\kappa(R^n) \subset P^n \backslash H(u_{n+1}).$$

Conversely, let p denote an arbitrary point of $P^n \backslash H(u_{n+1})$ and consider any set of coordinates $(x_1, \ldots, x_n, x_{n+1})$ of p. Since p is not in the hyperplane $H(u_{n+1})$, it follows that $x_{n+1} \neq 0$. Hence we may take

$$\lambda = 1/x_{n+1}$$

and obtain another set of coordinates

$$(y_1, \ldots, y_n, y_{n+1}) = \lambda(x_1, \ldots, x_n, x_{n+1})$$

for the point p. Then we have

$$y_{n+1} = \lambda x_{n+1} = 1.$$

Let $y = (y_1, \ldots, y_n) \, \epsilon \, R^n$. Then we obtain

$$\kappa(y) = \pi(y_1, \ldots, y_n, y_{n+1}) = p.$$

Since p is an arbitrary point of the set $P^n \backslash H(u_{n+1})$, this proves

$$P^n \backslash H(u_{n+1}) \subset \kappa(R^n).$$

Hence we obtain

$$\kappa(R^n) = P^n \backslash H(u_{n+1})$$

and the proof of (2.3) is now complete. $\|$

By means of the injective function $\kappa : R^n \to P^n$, we may identify R^n as the subset $P^n \backslash H(u_{n+1})$. If this is the case, the projective hyperplane $H(u_{n+1})$ is called the *hyperplane at infinity* of the Euclidean space R^n in the projective space P^n. The injective function

$$\kappa : R^n \to P^n$$

will be referred to as the *imbedding* of the Euclidean space R^n in the projective space P^n with the projective hyperplane $H(u_{n+1})$ as the hyperplane at infinity. For definiteness, we will always consider R^n as imbedded in P^n in this special way although R^n can be imbedded in P^n with an arbitrarily given projective hyperplane of P^n as the hyperplane at infinity.

EXERCISES

2A. Consider the unit n-sphere S^n in the $(n + 1)$-dimensional Euclidean space R^{n+1} defined by

$$S^n = \{x \in R^{n+1} \mid \| x \| = 1\}.$$

Then we have $S^n \subset W = R^{n+1} \setminus \{0\}$ and hence the restriction

$$\sigma = \pi \mid S^n : S^n \to P^n$$

of the natural projection $\pi : W \to P^n$ is well-defined. Prove that σ is surjective and that, for every point $p \in P^n$, the inverse image $\sigma^{-1}(p)$ in S^n consists of a pair of antipodal points of S^n. Hence the points of the projective space P^n may be considered as the pairs of antipodal points of S^n.

2B. Let p and q denote any two distinct points of P^n. Select coordinates $x = (x_1, \ldots, x_n, x_{n+1})$ and $y = (y_1, \ldots, y_n, y_{n+1})$ for the points p and q, respectively. Prove that the subset

$$\{\pi(\xi x + \eta y) \mid \xi \in R, \eta \in R, \xi^2 + \eta^2 > 0\}$$

of P^n depends only on the given points p and q of P^n. This subset of P^n is called the *projective line* of P^n determined by the points p and q and will be denoted by $\Lambda(p, q)$. Prove that

$$\Lambda(r, s) = \Lambda(p, q)$$

holds for any two distinct points r and s on $\Lambda(p, q)$. A subset Λ of P^n is said to be a *projective line* iff there exist two distinct points p and q of Λ satisfying

$$\Lambda = \Lambda(p, q).$$

2C. Consider R^n as imbedded in P^n with $H = H(u_{n+1})$ as the hyperplane at infinity. Prove that the intersection $\Lambda \cap R^n$ of any projective line Λ of P^n with R^n is a straight line of R^n iff Λ is not contained in H. On the other hand, prove that, for each straight line L of R^n, there exists a unique projective line Λ of P^n satisfying

$$\Lambda \cap R^n = L.$$

This projective line Λ is said to be *determined* by the straight line and will be denoted by $\Lambda(L)$. Prove that $H \cap \Lambda(L)$ is a single point, which will be called the *point at infinity* of the straight line L. Prove that two straight lines in R^n are parallel iff they have the same point at infinity.

2D. Three points p, q, r of P^n are said to be *collinear* iff there exists a projective line Λ in P^n which contains each of them; otherwise,

p, q, r are said to be *noncollinear*. For any three points p, q, r of P^n with $p \neq q$, prove that p, q, r are collinear iff there are coordinates $x = (x_1, \ldots, x_n, x_{n+1})$ and $y = (y_1, \ldots, y_n, y_{n+1})$ for the points p and q, respectively, such that $x + y$ is a set of coordinates of the point r.

3. METRIC GEOMETRY

To avoid higher dimensional complications which might obscure the geometrical ideas, we will restrict our studies in the remainder of the chapter to the two-dimensional spaces R^2 and P^2.

In the present section, we are concerned with the *Euclidean plane* R^2.

By definition, the *points* of R^2 are the ordered pairs (x, y) of real numbers x and y. The *addition* and the *scalar multiplication* in R^2 are given by

$$\lambda(u, v) + \mu(x, y) = (\lambda u + \mu x, \lambda v + \mu y)$$

for any two real numbers λ, μ and any two points (u, v), (x, y) of R^2. The *inner product* of R^2 is given by

$$(u, v) \cdot (x, y) = ux + vy$$

for any two points (u, v) and (x, y) of R^2. The *norm* in R^2 is defined by

$$\| (x, y) \| = \sqrt{(x^2 + y^2)}$$

for every point (x, y) of R^2. The *metric*

$$d : R^2 \times R^2 \to R$$

in R^2 is defined by

$$d[(u, v), (x, y)] = \sqrt{[(x - u)^2 + (y - v)^2]}$$

for any two points (u, v) and (x, y) of R^2.

According to Exercise 1F, the lines of R^2 are precisely the hyperplanes of R^2. Thus, a subset L of R^2 is a line iff there exist three real numbers a, b, c such that we have

$$a^2 + b^2 > 0$$

and

$$L = \{(x, y) \in R^2 \mid ax + by + c = 0\}.$$

The linear equation

$$ax + by + c = 0$$

is called an *equation of the line* L. In particular, the two coordinate axes X and Y are lines of R^2 defined by the equations $y = 0$ and $x = 0$, respectively. These two coordinate axes of R^2 meet at a single point, namely, the origin $(0, 0)$ of R^2. In symbols, we have

$$X \cap Y = (0, 0).$$

By an *isometric transformation* of the Euclidean plane R^2, we mean a bijective function

$$T:R^2 \to R^2$$

which preserves distance; that is,

$$d[T(u, v), T(x, y)] = d[(u, v), (x, y)]$$

holds for any two points (u, v) and (x, y) of the Euclidean plane R^2.

EXAMPLES OF ISOMETRIC TRANSFORMATIONS

(**1**) *Translations.* Let (a, b) denote an arbitrarily given point of R^2. Define a function

$$T:R^2 \to R^2$$

by taking

$$T(x, y) = (x + a, y + b)$$

for every point (x, y) of R^2. It can easily be verified that T is bijective and preserves distance. Hence T is an isometric transformation of R^2 called the *translation of R^2 which carries the origin $(0, 0)$ of R^2 to the given point (a, b).*

(**2**) *Rotations.* Let θ denote an arbitrarily given angle, positive, negative, or zero. Define a function

$$T:R^2 \to R^2$$

by taking

$$T(x, y) = (x \cos \theta - y \sin \theta, x \sin \theta + y \cos \theta)$$

for every point (x, y) of R^2. It can be easily verified that T is bijective and preserves distance. Hence T is an isometric transformation of R^2 called the *rotation of R^2 of an angle θ about the origin $(0, 0)$ of R^2.* The relative positions of the points (x, y) and $T(x, y)$ can be indicated by the following figure.

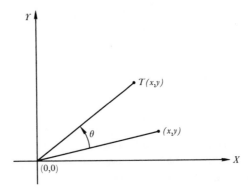

FIGURE 8

(3) *Reflections.* Define a function

$$T:R^2 \rightarrow R^2$$

by taking

$$T(x, y) = (x, -y)$$

for every point (x, y) of R^2. It can be easily verified that T is bijective and preserves distance. Hence T is an isometric transformation of R^2 called the *reflection of R^2 in the X-axis*. For each point (x, y) of R^2, the image $T(x, y)$ is the mirror image of (x, y) in the X-axis as indicated by the following figure.

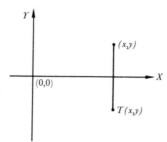

FIGURE 9

Similarly, one can define the *reflection of R^2 in the Y-axis;* in fact, one can define the *reflection of R^2 in any line.*

LEMMA 3.1. *If $T:R^2 \rightarrow R^2$ is an isometric transformation of R^2, then the image $T(L)$ of any line L in R^2 is a line in R^2.*

Proof. Let L denote an arbitrarily given line in R^2, and select any two distinct points a and b of R^2. By Exercise 1A, we have

$$L = L(a, b).$$

Since T is bijective, the two points $T(a)$ and $T(b)$ are distinct and hence determine a line $L[T(a), T(b)]$ in R^2. It remains to prove that

$$T(L) = L[T(a), T(b)].$$

For this purpose, let x denote any point of L. By the definition of $L(a, b)$ in Exercise 1A, there exists a real number λ satisfying

$$x = (1 - \lambda)a + \lambda(b).$$

In case $0 \leqslant \lambda \leqslant 1$, it follows from the assertion **(i)** of (1.13) that

$$d(a, b) = d(a, x) + d(b, x)$$

holds. Since T preserves distance, this implies

$$d[T(a), T(b)] = d[T(a), T(x)] + d[T(b), T(x)].$$

According to Assertion (**i**) of (1.13), this implies the existence of a real number μ satisfying

$$T(x) = (1 - \mu)\,T(a) + \mu\,T(b).$$

Hence, in this case, $T(x)$ is a point of the line $L[T(a),\ T(b)]$.

In case $\lambda \geqslant 1$, it follows from Assertion (**ii**) of (1.13) that

$$d(a,\ b) = d(a,\ x) - d(b,\ x)$$

holds. Since T preserves distance, this implies

$$d[T(a),\ T(b)] = d[T(a),\ T(x)] - d[T(b),\ T(x)].$$

According to Assertion (**ii**) of (1.13), this implies the existence of a real number μ satisfying

$$T(x) = (1 - \mu)\,T(a) + \mu\,T(b).$$

Hence, in this case, $T(x)$ is also a point of the line $L[T(a),\ T(b)]$.

In case $\lambda \leqslant 0$, it follows from Assertion (**iii**) of (1.13) that

$$d(a,\ b) = d(b,\ x) - d(a,\ x)$$

holds. Since T preserves distance, this implies

$$d[T(a),\ T(b)] = d[T(b),\ T(x)] - d[T(a),\ T(x)].$$

According to Assertion (**iii**) of (1.13), this implies the existence of a real number μ satisfying

$$T(x) = (1 - \mu)\,T(a) + \mu\,T(b).$$

Hence, in this case, $T(x)$ is also a point of the line $L[T(a),\ T(b)]$.

Summarizing the preceding three cases, we conclude that the image $T(x)$ of any point $x \in L(a,\ b)$ is a point of the line $L[T(a),\ T(b)]$. This proves

$$T(L) \subset L[T(a),\ T(b)].$$

Next, let y denote any point of the line $L[T(a),\ T(b)]$. We will prove the existence of a point $x \in L(a,\ b)$ with $T(x) = y$.

For this purpose, let us consider the inverse

$$T^{-1} : R^2 \to R^2$$

of the bijective function $T : R^2 \to R^2$. It is obvious that T^{-1} is bijective and preserves distance. Thus T^{-1} is also an isometric transformation of R^2. By what we have already proved, this implies that the image

$$x = T^{-1}(y)$$

of the point $y \in L[T(a),\ T(b)]$ is on the line

$$L[T^{-1}T(a),\ T^{-1}T(b)] = L(a,\ b).$$

Hence we obtain $x \in L(a, b)$ with

$$T(x) = T[T^{-1}(y)] = y.$$

This implies

$$T(L) = L[T(a), T(b)]$$

and completes the proof of (3.1).‖

LEMMA 3.2. *If $T:R^2 \to R^2$ is an isometric transformation of R^2, then*

$$T[(1 - \lambda)a + \lambda b] = (1 - \lambda)T(a) + \lambda T(b)$$

holds for every real number λ and any two points a, b of R^2.

Proof. If $a = b$, then the equality holds trivially. Hereafter in the proof, we assume $a \neq b$. Let

$$x = (1 - \lambda)a + \lambda b.$$

Since x is a point of the line $L(a, b)$, it follows from (3.1) that $T(x)$ is a point of the line $L[T(a), T(b)]$. Hence there exists a real number μ satisfying

$$T(x) = (1 - \mu)T(a) + \mu T(b).$$

It remains to prove that $\mu = \lambda$. For this purpose, let us consider the distances:

$$d(a, x) = \| x - a \| = \| \lambda(b - a) \| = | \lambda | \, d(a, b),$$
$$d(b, x) = \| b - x \| = \| (1 - \lambda)(b - a)\| = | 1 - \lambda | \, d(a, b).$$

Similarly, we have

$$d[T(a), T(x)] = | \mu | \, d[T(a), T(b)].$$
$$d[T(b), T(x)] = | 1 - \mu | \, d[T(a), T(b)].$$

Since T preserves distance, it follows that we have

$$d[T(a), T(b)] = d(a, b),$$
$$d[T(a), T(x)] = d(a, x),$$
$$d[T(b), T(x)] = d(b, x).$$

These imply the following two equalities:

$$| \mu | = | \lambda |, \qquad | 1 - \mu | = | 1 - \lambda |.$$

In case $| \lambda | \leq 1$, then we also have $| \mu | \leq 1$. These imply $1 - \mu \geq 0$ and $1 - \lambda \geq 0$. Hence we obtain

$$1 - \mu = | 1 - \mu | = | 1 - \lambda | = 1 - \lambda.$$

This implies $\mu = \lambda$.

In case $\lambda > 1$, we have $|1 - \lambda| = \lambda - 1$. Since $|\mu| = |\lambda| = \lambda$, we must have either $\mu = \lambda$ or $\mu = -\lambda$. To prove $\mu = \lambda$, let us assume $\mu = -\lambda$. Then we have

$$|1 - \mu| = |1 + \lambda| = 1 + \lambda > |1 - \lambda|.$$

This contradicts $|1 - \mu| = |1 - \lambda|$ and proves $\mu = \lambda$.

In case $\lambda < -1$, we have $|1 - \lambda| = 1 - \lambda$. Since $|\mu| = |\lambda| = -\lambda$, we must have either $\mu = \lambda$ or $\mu = -\lambda$. To prove $\mu = \lambda$, let us assume $\mu = -\lambda$. Then we have $\mu > 1$ and hence

$$|1 - \mu| = \mu - 1 = -\lambda - 1 < |1 - \lambda|.$$

This contradicts $|1 - \mu| = |1 - \lambda|$ and proves $\mu = \lambda$.

Summarizing the preceding three cases, we obtain $\mu = \lambda$. This completes the proof of (3.2).$\|$

Now let us consider the *orthogonal projections*

$$p:R^2 \to R, \qquad q:R^2 \to R$$

of the Euclidean plane R^2 onto its coordinate axes defined by

$$p(x, y) = x, \qquad q(x, y) = y$$

for every point (x, y) of R^2. For an arbitrarily given isometric transformation

$$T:R^2 \to R^2$$

of the Euclidean plane R^2, the compositions

$$\xi_T = p \circ T:R^2 \to R,$$
$$\eta_T = q \circ T:R^2 \to R$$

are real-valued functions on R^2 and will be called the *functions* (or *equations*) of the isometric transformation T. For an arbitrary point (x, y) of R^2, the real numbers $\xi_T(x, y)$ and $\eta_T(x, y)$ are the coordinates of the point $T(x, y)$; in symbols, we have

$$T(x, y) = [\xi_T(x, y), \eta_T(x, y)].$$

THEOREM 3.3. *For an arbitrarily given isometric transformation*

$$T:R^2 \to R^2,$$

there exists a point $(a, b) \in R^2$, *an angle* θ, *and a real number* ε *with* $|\varepsilon| = 1$ *such that*

$$\xi_T(x, y) = x \cos \theta - \varepsilon y \sin \theta + a,$$
$$\eta_T(x, y) = x \sin \theta + \varepsilon y \cos \theta + b$$

hold for every point (x, y) *of* R^2.

Proof. Consider the inverse

$$T^{-1}:R^2 \to R^2$$

of the bijective function $T:R^2 \to R^2$. Since T^{-1} is also an isometric transformation of R^2, it follows from (3.1) that the image

$$L = T^{-1}(\varUpsilon)$$

of the $\varUpsilon$-axis of R^2 is a line in R^2. Let (x, y) denote an arbitrary point of R^2. Then $(x, y) \in L$ iff $\xi_T(x, y) = 0$. This implies that

$$\xi_T(x, y) = 0$$

is an equation of the line. In view of (3.1) and (3.2), this implies that $\xi_T(x, y)$ is a linear polynomial of x and y. Precisely, there exist three real numbers a_1, a_2, and a such that

$$\xi_T(x, y) = a_1 x + a_2 y + a$$

holds for every point (x, y) of R^2. Similarly, there exist three real numbers b_1, b_2, and b such that

$$\eta_T(x, y) = b_1 x + b_2 y + b$$

holds for every point (x, y) of R^2. Then the real numbers a and b are clearly the coordinates of the image

$$T(0, 0) = (a, b)$$

of the origin $(0, 0)$ of R^2.

Let (x, y) denote an arbitrary point of R^2. Since T preserves distance, we have

$$d[T(0, 0), T(x, y)] = d[(0, 0), (x, y)].$$

This implies

$$(a_1 x + a_2 y)^2 + (b_1 x + b_2 y)^2 = x^2 + y^2.$$

Since this holds for every point (x, y) of R^2, we must have

$$a_1^2 + b_1^2 = 1, \qquad a_2^2 + b_2^2 = 1, \qquad a_1 a_2 + b_1 b_2 = 0.$$

Because of the first two of these equalities, there exist two angles θ and ω such that

$$a_1 = \cos \theta, \qquad b_1 = \sin \theta,$$
$$a_2 = \cos \omega, \qquad b_2 = \sin \omega.$$

Then the equality $a_1 a_2 + b_1 b_2$ becomes

$$\cos (\omega - \theta) = \cos \omega \cos \theta + \sin \omega \sin \theta = 0.$$

This implies

$$\omega - \theta = 2k\pi \pm \pi/2,$$

where k is an integer.

In case $\omega - \theta = 2k\pi + \pi/2$, we obtain

$$\cos \omega = -\sin \theta, \qquad \sin \omega = \cos \theta.$$

In this case, we have $\varepsilon = 1$ and

$$\xi_T(x, y) = x \cos \theta - y \sin \theta + a,$$
$$\eta_T(x, y) = x \sin \theta + y \cos \theta + b.$$

In case $\omega - \theta = 2k\pi - \pi/2$, we obtain

$$\cos \omega = \sin \theta, \qquad \sin \omega = -\cos \theta.$$

In this case, we have $\varepsilon = -1$ and

$$\xi_T(x, y) = x \cos \theta + y \sin \theta + a,$$
$$\eta_T(x, y) = x \sin \theta - y \cos \theta + b.$$

This completes the proof of (3.3).‖

As the converse of (3.3), we have the following proposition.

PROPOSITION 3.4. *For any point (a, b) of R^2, any angle θ, and any real number ε with $|\varepsilon| = 1$, the function*

$$T : R^2 \to R^2$$

defined by

$$T(x, y) = (x \cos \theta - \varepsilon y \sin \theta + a, \ x \sin \theta + \varepsilon y \cos \theta + b)$$

for every point (x, y) of R^2 is an isometric transformation of R^2.

Proof. In case $\varepsilon = 1$, T is the composition of a rotation about the origin and a translation. In case $\varepsilon = -1$, T is the composition of a reflection in the X-axis, a rotation about the origin, and a translation. Since the composition of a finite number of isometric transformations of R^2 is clearly an isometric transformation of R^2, this proves (3.4).‖

The set of all isometric transformations of R^2 forms a group with composition as the group operation. This group will be referred to as the *isometry group* of the Euclidean plane. The following proposition is obvious from the proofs of (3.3) and (3.4).

PROPOSITION 3.5. *The isometry group of R^2 is generated by the translations, the rotations about the origin, and the reflection in the X-axis.*

A property of a subset of R^2 is said to be a *metric property* iff it is preserved by every isometric transformation of R^2.

By the *metric geometry* of R^2, or the *Euclidean geometry* of R^2, we mean the branch of mathematics which studies the metric properties of subsets of R^2.

EXAMPLES OF METRIC PROPERTIES

(i)   Distance between two points.
(ii) Parallelism of two lines.
(iii) Perpendicularity of two lines.
(iv) Area of a triangle.
(v)   Cosine of the angle between two directed lines.

EXERCISES

3A. The isometric transformation $T:R^2 \to R^2$ in (3.4) is called a *rigid
motion* of the Euclidean plane R^2. Prove that the set H of all rigid
motions of R^2 is a subgroup of the isometry group G of R^2. Let r
denote the reflection of R^2 in the X-axis. Prove that

$$G = H \cup Hr.$$

Hence H is a normal subgroup of G and the quotient group G/H is a
cyclic group of order two.

3B. Prove that three points (x_1, y_1), (x_2, y_2), and (x_3, y_3) are collinear iff

$$\begin{vmatrix} x_1 & y_1 & 1 \\ x_2 & y_2 & 1 \\ x_3 & y_3 & 1 \end{vmatrix} = 0.$$

3C. Three lines L_1, L_2, L_3 of R^2 are said to be *concurrent* iff

$$L_1 \cap L_2 \cap L_3 \neq \square.$$

Let $a_i x + b_i y + c_i = 0$ denote an equation of the line L_i for every
$i = 1, 2, 3$. Prove that

$$\begin{vmatrix} a_1 & b_1 & c_1 \\ a_2 & b_2 & c_2 \\ a_3 & b_3 & c_3 \end{vmatrix} = 0$$

holds if L_1, L_2, L_3 are concurrent. Investigate the converse of this
statement.

4. PROJECTIVE GEOMETRY

In the present section, we are concerned with the *projective plane* P^2.
To recall briefly the construction of P^2, consider the three-dimensional Euclidean space R^3. The points of R^3 are the ordered triples

$$x = (x_1, x_2, x_3)$$

of real numbers. The point $O = (0, 0, 0)$ is called the origin of R^3. In the subset

$$W = R^3 \setminus \{O\}$$

of R^3, there is an equivalence relation $\sim$ defined as follows: for any two points x and y of W, $x \sim y$ iff there exists a nonzero real number λ with $y = \lambda x$. Then

$$P^2 = W/\sim$$

is the set of all equivalence classes in W. Let

$$\pi : W \to P^2$$

denote the natural projection. The points

$$v_1 = \pi(1, 0, 0), \qquad v_2 = \pi(0, 1, 0), \qquad v_3 = \pi(0, 0, 1)$$

are called the *coordinate vertices* of P^2, and the point

$$v = \pi(1, 1, 1)$$

will be referred to as the *unit point* of P^2.

By a *linear transformation* of R^3, we mean a bijective linear mapping

$$\alpha : R^3 \to R^3$$

of the vector space R^3 onto itself as defined in (III, §5). Since α is bijective and satisfies $\alpha(O) = O$, it follows that we have

$$\alpha(W) = W$$

and hence we may define a bijective function

$$\alpha^* : W \to W$$

by taking $\alpha^*(x) = \alpha(x)$ for every point x of W.

LEMMA 4.1.   *For any two points x and y, we have $\alpha^*(x) \sim \alpha^*(y)$ iff $x \sim y$.*

Proof. Sufficiency. Assume $x \sim y$. Then there exists a nonzero real number λ satisfying $y = \lambda x$. Since α is a linear mapping, we have

$$\alpha^*(y) = \alpha(y) = \alpha(\lambda x) = \lambda\alpha(x) = \lambda\alpha^*(x).$$

This implies $\alpha^*(x) \sim \alpha^*(y)$.

Necessity. Assume $\alpha^*(x) \sim \alpha^*(y)$. Then there exists a nonzero real number λ satisfying $\alpha^*(y) = \lambda\alpha^*(x)$. Since α is a linear mapping, we have

$$\alpha^*(\lambda x) = \alpha(\lambda x) = \lambda\alpha(x) = \lambda\alpha^*(x) = \alpha^*(y).$$

Since α^* is bijective, this implies $y = \lambda x$. Hence we obtain $x \sim y$. $\|$

It follows from (4.1) that the image $\alpha^*(p)$ of every equivalence class p in W is an equivalence class in W. Since P^2 is the set of all equivalence classes in W, the assignment

$$p \to \alpha^*(p)$$

defines a bijective function

$$T_\alpha:P^2 \to P^2,$$

which is called the *projective transformation* of the projective plane P^2 determined by the linear transformation α of R^3.

Since compositions and inverses of linear transformations of R^3 are linear transformations of R^3, it follows that the set of all projective transformations of the projective plane P^2 forms a group with composition as the group operation. This group will be referred to as the *projectile group* of P^2.

A property of a subset of P^2 is said to be a *projective property* iff it is preserved by every projective transformation of P^2. For example, the collinearity of three points of P^2 is a projective property.

By the *projective geometry* of P^2, we mean the branch of mathematics which studies the projective properties of subsets of P^2.

Now let us consider an arbitrarily given projective transformation

$$T_\alpha:P^2 \to P^2$$

determined by a linear transformation

$$\alpha:R^3 \to R^3.$$

For every integer $i = 1, 2, 3$, let

$$p_i:R^3 \to R$$

denote the orthogonal projection of R^3 onto its ith coordinate axis defined by

$$p_i(x_1, x_2, x_3) = x_i$$

for every point (x_1, x_2, x_3) of R^3. Then the three composed functions

$$\alpha_i = p_i \circ \alpha:R^3 \to R \qquad (i = 1, 2, 3)$$

are called the *functions*, or *equations*, of the linear transformation α. For an arbitrary point $x \in R^3$, $\alpha_i(x)$ is the ith coordinate of the point $\alpha(x)$; in symbols, we have

$$\alpha(x) = [\alpha_1(x), \alpha_2(x), \alpha_3(x)].$$

The images $\alpha(u_1)$, $\alpha(u_2)$, $\alpha(u_3)$ of the unit points

$$u_1 = (1, 0, 0), \qquad u_2 = (0, 1, 0), \qquad u_3 = (0, 0, 1)$$

on the coordinate axes of R^3 are points of R^3. For each $i = 1, 2, 3$, let the coordinates of the point $\alpha(u_i)$ be denoted by

$$\alpha(u_i) = (a_{1i}, a_{2i}, a_{3i}).$$

LEMMA 4.2. *The function α_1, α_2, α_3 of the linear transformation $\alpha : R^3 \rightarrow R$ is given by*

$$\alpha_i(x) = \sum_{j=1}^{3} a_{ij}x_j \qquad (i = 1, 2, 3)$$

for every point $x = (x_1, x_2, x_3)$ of R^3.

Proof. Let $x = (x_1, x_2, x_3)$ denote an arbitrary point of R^3. Then we have

$$x = \sum_{j=1}^{3} x_j u_j.$$

Since α is a linear mapping, this implies

$$\alpha(x) = \sum_{j=1}^{3} x_j \alpha(u_j).$$

Equating the coordinates of both sides, we obtain

$$\alpha_i(x) = \sum_{j=1}^{3} a_{ij}x_j \qquad (i = 1, 2, 3).$$

This proves (4.2).‖

The three-by-three matrix

$$M(\alpha) = \begin{pmatrix} a_{11} & a_{12} & a_{13} \\ a_{21} & a_{22} & a_{23} \\ a_{31} & a_{32} & a_{33} \end{pmatrix}$$

of real numbers a_{ij} is called the *matrix* of the linear transformation α. Since α is bijective, $M(\alpha)$ must be *nonsingular;* that is, its determinant

$$\det [M(\alpha)] = \begin{vmatrix} a_{11} & a_{12} & a_{13} \\ a_{21} & a_{22} & a_{23} \\ a_{31} & a_{32} & a_{33} \end{vmatrix}$$

must be different from zero.

The matrix $M(\alpha)$ is also called a *matrix* of the projective transformation T_α of the projective plane P^2. It determines T_α completely. However, for any nonzero real number λ, the matrix

$$\lambda M(\alpha) = \begin{pmatrix} \lambda a_{11} & \lambda a_{12} & \lambda a_{13} \\ \lambda a_{21} & \lambda a_{22} & \lambda a_{23} \\ \lambda a_{31} & \lambda a_{32} & \lambda a_{33} \end{pmatrix}$$

is also a matrix of the same projective transformation T_α of P^2.

LEMMA 4.3. *Three points p, q, r of P^2 with coordinates*

$$(a_1, a_2, a_3), \qquad (b_1, b_2, b_3), \qquad (c_1, c_2, c_3)$$

respectively are collinear iff

$$\begin{vmatrix} a_1 & b_1 & c_1 \\ a_2 & b_2 & c_2 \\ a_3 & b_3 & c_3 \end{vmatrix} = 0.$$

Proof. Since the lemma is trivial when p, q, r are not distinct, we may assume that p, q, r are distinct. In this case, p, q, r are collinear iff (c_1, c_2, c_3) is a linear combination of (a_1, a_2, a_3) and (b_1, b_2, b_3) according to Exercise 2B. By elementary linear algebra, this is equivalent to

$$\begin{vmatrix} a_1 & b_1 & c_1 \\ a_2 & b_2 & c_2 \\ a_3 & b_3 & c_3 \end{vmatrix} = 0.$$

This proves (4.3).‖

To conclude the present section, let us establish the following theorem of projective transformations of P^2.

THEOREM 4.4. *If p_1, p_2, p_3, and p are four points of P^2 such that no three of these are collinear, then there exists a unique projective transformation*

$$T:P^2 \to P^2$$

satisfying

$$T(v_1) = p_1, \qquad T(v_2) = p_2, \qquad T(v_3) = p_3, \qquad T(v) = p.$$

Proof. Choose coordinates

$$(a_1, a_2, a_3), \qquad (b_1, b_2, b_3), \qquad (c_1, c_2, c_3), \qquad (d_1, d_2, d_3)$$

for the points p_1, p_2, p_3, p, respectively.

To prove the existence of T, let ξ, η, ζ denote arbitrary nonzero real numbers to be determined later. Consider the function

$$\alpha:R^3 \to R^3$$

defined for every $x = (x_1, x_2, x_3) \in R^3$ by

$$\alpha(x) = [\alpha_1(x), \alpha_2(x), \alpha_3(x)]$$

with

$$\alpha_i(x) = \xi a_i x_1 + \eta b_i x_2 + \zeta c_i x_3 \qquad (i = 1, 2, 3).$$

This function α is obviously a linear mapping. On the other hand, since the points p_1, p_2, p_3 are not collinear and the real numbers ξ, η, ζ are nonzero, it follows from (4.3) that α is also bijective. Hence α is a linear transformation of R^3 and defines a projective transformation

$$T_\alpha : P^2 \to P^2.$$

This projective transformation T_α of P^2 carries v into p if

$$\alpha_i(u) = \xi a_i + \eta b_i + \zeta c_i = d_i$$

holds for every $i = 1, 2, 3$. Since no three of the points p_1, p_2, p_3, p are collinear, the system of linear equations

$$a_i \xi + b_i \eta + c_i \zeta = d_i \qquad (i = 1, 2, 3)$$

has a unique solution (ξ, η, ζ) with $\xi \neq 0$, $\eta \neq 0$, and $\zeta \neq 0$. With these ξ, η, ζ, the projective transformation T_α carries v_1, v_2, v_3, v to p_1, p_2, p_3, p, respectively. This proves existence.

To prove uniqueness, let

$$T = T_\beta : P^2 \to P^2$$

denote an arbitrary projective transformation of P^2 which carries v_1, v_2, v_3, v to p_1, p_2, p_3, p, respectively. Let

$$M(\beta) = \begin{pmatrix} e_{11} & e_{12} & e_{13} \\ e_{21} & e_{22} & e_{23} \\ e_{31} & e_{32} & e_{33} \end{pmatrix}$$

denote the matrix of the linear transformation

$$\beta : R^3 \to R^3.$$

Since T carries v_1 into p_1, it follows that (e_{11}, e_{21}, e_{31}) is a set of coordinates of p_1. Hence there is a nonzero real number ξ' such that

$$(e_{11}, e_{21}, e_{31}) = (\xi' a_1, \xi' a_2, \xi' a_3)$$

holds. Similarly, there exist nonzero real numbers η' and ζ' satisfying

$$(e_{12}, e_{22}, e_{32}) = (\eta' b_1, \eta' b_2, \eta' b_3),$$
$$(e_{13}, e_{23}, e_{33}) = (\zeta' c_1, \zeta' c_2, \zeta' c_3).$$

Since T carries v to p, it follows that

$$(e_{11} + e_{12} + e_{13}, e_{21} + e_{22} + e_{23}, e_{31} + e_{32} + e_{33})$$

is a set of coordinates for the point p. Hence there exists a nonzero real number λ satisfying

$$e_{i1} + e_{i2} + e_{i3} = \lambda d_i$$

for every $i = 1, 2, 3$. This implies that the real numbers ξ', η', ζ' satisfy the linear equations

$$a_i\xi' + b_i\eta' + c_i\zeta' = \lambda d_i \qquad (i = 1, 2, 3).$$

Thus we obtain $\xi' = \lambda\xi$, $\eta' = \lambda\eta$, $\zeta' = \lambda\zeta$ and hence

$$M(\beta) = \lambda M(\alpha).$$

This implies $T_\beta = T_\alpha$ and completes the proof.$\|$

EXERCISES

4A. Let p, q, r, s denote arbitrarily given distinct collinear points of P^2. Show that one can find two points a, b of $W = R^3 \setminus \{O\}$ and a real number λ satisfying

$$\pi(a) = p, \qquad \pi(b) = q, \qquad \pi(a + b) = r, \qquad \pi(a + \lambda b) = s.$$

Prove that the real number λ depends only on the ordered set (p, q, r, s). This real number λ is called the *cross ratio* of (p, q, r, s) and will be denoted by

$$\lambda = \chi(p, q, r, s).$$

Prove that $\chi(p, q, r, s)$ is a projective property of (p, q, r, s). The ordered set $(p, q; r, s)$ is said to be a *harmonic range* iff

$$\chi(p, q, r, s) = -1.$$

4B. Prove that a subset Λ of P^2 is a projective line iff there exists a point $a = (a_1, a_2, a_3)$ of $W = R^3 \setminus \{O\}$ such that a point $p \in P^2$ is in Λ iff

$$a \cdot x = a_1x_1 + a_2x_2 + a_3x_3 = 0$$

holds for every $x = (x_1, x_2, x_3) \in W$ with $\pi(x) = p$. The homogeneous linear equation

$$a_1x_1 + a_2x_2 + a_3x_3 = 0$$

in x_1, x_2, x_3 is called an *equation* for the projective line Λ. Prove that

$$b_1x_1 + b_2x_2 + b_3x_3 = 0$$

is an equation for the same projective line Λ iff there exists a nonzero real number λ satisfying

$$b_i = \lambda a_i \qquad (i = 1, 2, 3).$$

Prove that the intersection of any two distinct projective lines in P^2 is a single point of P^2.

4C. Let $T:P^2 \to P^2$ be an arbitrary projective transformation of P^2. Prove that the image $T(\Lambda)$ of any projective line Λ of P^2 is a projective line. Hence collinearity of points in P^2 is a projective property.

4D. A family of projective lines in P^2 is said to be *concurrent* iff their intersection is nonempty. Prove that the concurrency of projective lines in P^2 is a projective property.

4E. Let α, β, γ, δ denote arbitrarily given distinct concurrent projective lines in P^2. Show that one can find two points a, b of W and a real number λ such that

$$a \cdot x = 0, \quad b \cdot x = 0, \quad (a + b) \cdot x = 0, \quad (a + \lambda b) \cdot x = 0,$$

with $x = (x_1, x_2, x_3)$, are equations of α, β, γ, δ, respectively. Prove that the real number λ depends only on the ordered set $(\alpha, \beta, \gamma, \delta)$. This real number λ is called the *cross ratio* of $(\alpha, \beta, \gamma, \delta)$ and will be denoted by

$$\lambda = \chi(\alpha, \beta, \gamma, \delta).$$

Prove that $\chi(\alpha, \beta, \gamma, \delta)$ is a projective property of $(\alpha, \beta, \gamma, \delta)$. The ordered set $(\alpha, \beta, \gamma, \delta)$ is said to be a *harmonic bundle* iff

$$\chi(\alpha, \beta, \gamma, \delta) = -1.$$

5. AFFINE GEOMETRY

Consider the Euclidean plane R^2 imbedded as a subset of the projective plane P^2 by means of the imbedding

$$\kappa : R^2 \to P^2$$

defined by

$$\kappa(x, y) = \pi(x, y, 1)$$

for every point (x, y) of R^2, where π denotes the natural projection of the subset

$$W = R^3 \backslash \{O\}$$

of the Euclidean space R^3 onto the projective plane P^2. In other words, we identify $(x, y) \in R^2$ with $\kappa(x, y) \in P^2$ and hence we have

$$R^2 = \kappa(R^2) \subset P^2.$$

According to (2.3), the complement

$$H(u_3) = P^2 \backslash R^2$$

is the coordinate hyperplane $H(u_3)$ of P^2. By definition of $H(u_3)$, a point

$p \in P^2$ is in $H(u_3)$ iff there exists $(x_1, x_2, x_3) \in W$ with $\pi(x_1, x_2, x_3) = p$ and $x_3 = 0$. Hence $H(u_3)$ is the projective line of P^2 defined by the equation

$$x_3 = 0.$$

This projective line is called the *line at infinity* of R^2 in P^2 and will be denoted by Λ_∞. Thus, we have

$$P^2 = R^2 \cup \Lambda_\infty, \qquad R^2 \cap \Lambda_\infty = \square.$$

By an *affine transformation* of the projective plane P^2, we mean a projective transformation

$$T : P^2 \to P^2$$

of P^2 satisfying

$$T(R^2) = R^2, \qquad T(\Lambda_\infty) = \Lambda_\infty.$$

Since the composition of any two affine transformations of P^2 and the inverse of any affine transformation of P^2 are obviously affine transformations of P^2, it follows that the set of all affine transformations of P^2 is a subgroup of the projective group of P^2 and will be called the *affine group of the projective plane P^2*.

A property of a subset of P^2 is said to be an *affine property* iff it is preserved by every affine transformation of P^2. For example, the concurrency of two projective lines with Λ_∞ is an affine property. Since the affine group of P^2 is a subgroup of the projective group of P^2, it follows that every projective property is also an affine property. The converse is false.

By the *affine geometry* of P^2, we mean the branch of mathematics which studies the affine properties of subsets of P^2.

Since projective transformations of P^2 are bijective and send projective lines onto projective lines, the following proposition is obvious.

PROPOSITION 5.1. *For an arbitrary projective transformation T of the projective plane P^2, the following three statements are equivalent:*

(i) T *is an affine transformation.*
(ii) $T(R^2) \subset R^2$.
(iii) $T(\Lambda_\infty) \subset \Lambda_\infty$.

Now let us consider an arbitrarily given projective transformation

$$T_\alpha : P^2 \to P^2$$

determined by a linear transformation

$$\alpha : R^3 \to R^3$$

with matrix

$$M(\alpha) = \begin{pmatrix} a_{11} & a_{12} & a_{13} \\ a_{21} & a_{22} & a_{23} \\ a_{31} & a_{32} & a_{33} \end{pmatrix}.$$

PROPOSITION 5.2. *The projective transformation* $T_\alpha : P^2 \to P^2$ *is an affine transformation of* P^2 *iff we have* $a_{31} = 0$ *and* $a_{32} = 0$.

Proof. *Necessity.* Assume that T_α is an affine transformation of P^2. Then we have

$$T_\alpha(\Lambda_\infty) \subset \Lambda_\infty.$$

Consider the two points $p = \pi(1, 0, 0)$ and $q = \pi(0, 1, 0)$. Since p and q are on Λ_∞, it follows that $T_\alpha(p)$ and $T_\alpha(q)$ are also on Λ_∞. This implies $\alpha_3(p) = 0$ and $\alpha_3(q) = 0$. Since we have

$$\alpha_3(p) = a_{31}, \qquad \alpha_3(q) = a_{32},$$

it follows that $a_{31} = 0$ and $a_{32} = 0$ hold.

Sufficiency. Assume $a_{31} = 0$ and $a_{32} = 0$. Let p denote an arbitrary point of Λ_∞ and choose a point $x = (x_1, x_2, x_3)$ of W with $\pi(x) = p$. Since p is on Λ_∞, we must have $x_3 = 0$. Hence we obtain

$$\alpha_3(x) = a_{31}x_1 + a_{32}x_2 + a_{33}x_3 = 0.$$

This implies $T_\alpha(p) \in \Lambda_\infty$. Thus we have proved

$$T_\alpha(\Lambda_\infty) \subset \Lambda_\infty.$$

According to (5.1), this implies that T_α is an affine transformation of P^2.‖

For an arbitrary affine transformation

$$T : P^2 \to P^2$$

of the projective plane P^2, it follows from the definition that we have

$$T(R^2) = R^2.$$

Consequently, T defines a bijective function

$$T^* : R^2 \to R^2$$

which will be called an *affine transformation* of the Euclidean plane R^2. Since the composition of any two affine transformations of R^2 and the inverse of any affine transformation of R^2 are obviously affine transformations of R^2, it follows that the set of all affine transformations of R^2 forms a group with composition as the group operation. This group is called the *affine group of the Euclidean plane* R^2.

By means of the uniqueness part in (4.4), one can easily verify that the assignment

$$T \to T^*$$

defines an isomorphism from the affine group of P^2 onto the affine group of R^2. Hence we may identify these two groups by means of this isomorphism. As a consequence of this identification, the affine group of R^2 becomes a subgroup of the projective group of P^2.

A property of a subset of R^2 is said to be an *affine property* iff it is preserved by every affine transformation of R^2.

By the *affine geometry* of R^2, we mean the branch of mathematics which studies the affine properties of subsets of R^2.

EXAMPLES OF AFFINE PROPERTIES

(**i**)   Parallelism of lines.
(**ii**) Concurrency of lines.
(**iii**) Collinearity of points.

To determine the equations of the affine transformations of R^2, we have the following theorem.

THEOREM 5.3.   *A bijective function*

$$S:R^2 \longrightarrow R^2$$

is an affine transformation of R^2 iff there exist real numbers a_1, b_1, c_1, a_2, b_2, c_2 satisfying

$$S(x, y) = (a_1x + b_1y + c_1, a_2x + b_2y + c_2)$$

for every point (x, y) of R^2.

Proof.   Necessity.   Assume that S is an affine transformation of R^2. Then there exists an affine transformation

$$T_\alpha:P^2 \longrightarrow P^2$$

of the projective plane P^2 determined by a linear transformation

$$\alpha:R^3 \longrightarrow R^3$$

such that $S = T_\alpha{}^*$ holds.

According to (5.2), the matrix

$$M(\alpha) = \begin{pmatrix} a_{11} & a_{12} & a_{13} \\ a_{21} & a_{22} & a_{23} \\ a_{31} & a_{32} & a_{33} \end{pmatrix}$$

of the linear transformation α satisfies

$$a_{31} = 0, \qquad a_{32} = 0.$$

Since T_α is bijective, we must have

$$a_{33} \neq 0.$$

Therefore, we may define

$$a_1 = a_{11}/a_{33}, \qquad b_1 = a_{12}/a_{33}, \qquad c_1 = a_{13}/a_{33},$$
$$a_2 = a_{21}/a_{33}, \qquad b_2 = a_{22}/a_{33}, \qquad c_2 = a_{23}/a_{33}.$$

To complete the necessity proof, let (x, y) denote an arbitrary point of R^2. From $S = T_\alpha{}^*$, it follows that we have

$$S = \kappa^{-1} \circ T_\alpha \circ \kappa,$$

where $\kappa : R^2 \to P^2$ denotes the imbedding defined at the beginning of the section. By definition, the point $\kappa(x, y)$ of P^2 has homogeneous coordinates

$$(x, y, 1).$$

Since T_α is determined by the linear transformation α, we have

$$
\begin{aligned}
T_\alpha[\kappa(x, y)] &= \pi[\alpha(x, y, 1)] \\
&= \pi(a_{11}x + a_{12}y + a_{13}, \, a_{21}x + a_{22}y + a_{23}, \, a_{33}) \\
&= \pi(a_1x + b_1y + c_1, \, a_2x + b_2y + c_2, \, 1),
\end{aligned}
$$

where $\pi : W \to P^2$ denotes the natural projection. Hence we obtain

$$
\begin{aligned}
S(x, y) &= \kappa^{-1}\{ T_\alpha[\kappa(x, y)] \} \\
&= \kappa^{-1}[\pi(a_1x + b_1y + c_1, \, a_2x + b_2y + c_2, \, 1)] \\
&= (a_1x + b_1y + c_1, \, a_2x + b_2y + c_2).
\end{aligned}
$$

This completes the necessity proof.

Sufficiency.   Assume that there exist real numbers $a_1, b_1, c_1, a_2, b_2, c_2$ satisfying

$$S(x, y) = (a_1x + b_1y + c_1, \, a_2x + b_2y + c_2)$$

for every point (x, y) of R^2. Since S is bijective, it follows that the determinant

$$
\begin{vmatrix}
a_1 & b_1 \\
a_2 & b_2
\end{vmatrix} = a_1b_2 - a_2b_1
$$

must be different from zero. Define a function

$$\alpha : R^3 \to R^3$$

by setting

$$\alpha(x_1, x_2, x_3) = (a_1x_1 + b_1x_2 + c_1x_3, \, a_2x_1 + b_2x_2 + c_2x_3, \, x_3)$$

for every point (x_1, x_2, x_3) of R^3. Because of

$$
\begin{vmatrix}
a_1 & b_1 & c_1 \\
a_2 & b_2 & c_2 \\
0 & 0 & 1
\end{vmatrix} = a_1b_2 - a_2b_1 \neq 0,
$$

α is a bijective linear mapping and hence, by definition, a linear transformation of the Euclidean space R^3.

According to the definition of the projective transformations of P^2, α determines a projective transformation

$$T_\alpha : P^2 \to P^2.$$

In view of (5.2), T_α is an affine transformation of the projective plane P^2. Since one can easily verify that

$$S = \kappa^{-1} \circ T_\alpha \circ \kappa,$$

it follows that S is an affine transformation of R^2. This completes the proof.‖

PROPOSITION 5.4. *The real numbers* a_1, b_1, c_1, a_2, b_2, c_2 *in* (5.3) *are completely determined by the affine transformation* $S: R^2 \to R^2$.

Proof. According to (5.3), the real numbers a_1, b_1, c_1, a_2, b_2, c_2 satisfy

$$S(x, y) = (a_1x + b_1y + c_1,\ a_2x + b_2y + c_2)$$

for every point (x, y) of R^2. Applying this equality to the points $(1, 0)$, $(0, 1)$, and $(0, 0)$ of R^2, we obtain

$$S(1, 0) = (a_1 + c_1,\ a_2 + c_2),$$
$$S(0, 1) = (b_1 + c_1,\ b_2 + c_2),$$
$$S(0, 0) = (c_1, c_2).$$

Therefore, we get

$$(a_1, a_2) = S(1, 0) - S(0, 0),$$
$$(b_1, b_2) = S(0, 1) - S(0, 0),$$
$$(c_1, c_2) = S(0, 0).$$

This proves that the real numbers a_1, b_1, c_1, a_2, b_2, c_2 are completely determined by S.‖

Because of (5.4), the real numbers a_1, b_1, a_2, b_2 in (5.3) are called the *coefficients* of the affine transformation S and the real numbers c_1, c_2 are called the *constant terms* of S.

The following proposition was proved in the sufficiency proof of (5.3).

PROPOSITION 5.5. *The coefficients* a_1, b_1, a_2, b_2 *of an affine transformation of* R^2 *satisfy*

$$a_1b_2 - a_2b_1 \neq 0.$$

Now let us consider the orthogonal projection

$$p: R^2 \to R, \qquad q: R^2 \to R$$

of the Euclidean plane R^2 onto its coordinate axes defined by

$$p(x, y) = x, \qquad q(x, y) = y$$

for every point (x, y) of R^2. For an arbitrary affine transformation

$$S: R^2 \to R^2$$

of the Euclidean plane R^2, the compositions

$$\xi_S = p \circ S : R^2 \to R,$$
$$\eta_S = q \circ S : R^2 \to R$$

are real-valued functions on R^2 and will be called the *functions* (or *equations*) of the affine transformation S.

The following proposition is obvious.

PROPOSITION 5.6. *If $S : R^2 \to R^2$ is an affine transformation of R^2 with coefficients a_1, b_1, a_2, b_2 and constant terms c_1, c_2, then we have*

$$\xi_S(x, y) = a_1 x + b_1 y + c_1,$$
$$\eta_S(x, y) = a_2 x + b_2 y + c_2$$

for every point (x, y) of R^2.

The following proposition is a direct consequence of (3.3) and (5.3).

PROPOSITION 5.7. *Every isometric transformation of the Euclidean plane R^2 is an affine transformation of R^2.*

Consequently, we have the following corollaries.

COROLLARY 5.8. *The isometric group of the Euclidean plane R^2 is a subgroup of the affine group of R^2 and hence is also a subgroup of the projective group of the projective plane P^2.*

COROLLARY 5.9. *Every affine property of a subset of the Euclidean plane R^2 is also a metric property.*

Thus, the affine geometry of the Euclidean plane R^2 is a part of the metric geometry of R^2.

Strictly speaking, there is no projective geometry of the Euclidean plane. However, every set F in R^2 studied in the classical Euclidean geometry can be considered as a part of a natural set F^* of the containing projective plane P^2. For example, if F is a straight line in R^2, then F^* is the unique projective line in P^2 which contains F. The points of

$$F^* \backslash F$$

are called the *points at infinity* of F. Thus a straight line in R^2 has a unique point at infinity. As another example, a conic section in R^2 has 0, 1, or 2 points at infinity according to whether it is an ellipse, a parabola, or a hyperbola. A property of F is said to be a *projective property* iff it is a projective property of F^*. For example, concurrency of lines and collinearity of points are projective properties. Then the *projective geometry* of R^2 is the branch of mathematics which studies the projective properties of subsets of R^2. Since every projective property is also an affine property, it follows that the projective geometry of R^2 is a part of the affine geometry of R^2.

EXERCISES

5A. Prove that an affine transformation of the Euclidean plane R^2 is an isometric transformation of R^2 iff its coefficients a_1, b_1, a_2, b_2 satisfy the following equalities:

$$a_1{}^2 + a_2{}^2 = 1, \qquad b_1{}^2 + b_2{}^2 = 1, \qquad a_1 b_1 + a_2 b_2 = 0.$$

5B. Find a necessary and sufficient condition that an affine transformation of the projective plane P^2 defines an isometric transformation of R^2.

5C. Generalize the geometries in §§3–5 to n dimensions.

5D. Generalize the results in this chapter by using an arbitrary field F instead of the field R of real numbers.

Chapter V: ELEMENTARY TOPOLOGY

In the first three sections of this final chapter, we will introduce the reader to the topology of metric spaces which are motivated by the Euclidean spaces studied in the preceding chapter. By merely passing to special cases, one will get the topology of Euclidean spaces and, in particular, of the real line R and the plane $C = R^2$ of the complex numbers. In the last section, we will define topological spaces and give a few topological properties. Interested readers will be able to study either of the author's two books on general topology for further information, namely, *Elements of General Topology* and *Introduction to General Topology*.

1. METRIC SPACES

The Euclidean spaces studied in (IV, §1) motivate a class of more general spaces called *metric spaces*.

To define the meaning of a metric space, let us consider an arbitrarily given set X. The members of X will be called points.

By a *metric*, or a *distance function*, in the set X, we mean a real-valued function

$$d:X \times X \to R$$

defined on the Cartesian square

$$X^2 = X \times X$$

such that the following two conditions are satisfied:

(**M1**) (*The triangle inequality.*) For any three points a, b, c in X, we have

$$d(a, c) + d(b, c) \geqslant d(a, b).$$

(**M2**) For any two points a, b in X, $d(a, b) = 0$ iff $a = b$.

LEMMA 1.1. *If $d:X^2 \to R$ is any metric in a set X, then we have*

(**M3**) $\qquad\qquad\qquad d(a, b) \geqslant 0$

(**M4**) $\qquad\qquad\qquad d(a, b) = d(b, a)$

for any two points a and b in X.

Proof. To establish (**M3**), we apply (**M1**) to the points a, a, b of X and get

$$2d(a, b) = d(a, b) + d(a, b) \geqslant d(a, a).$$

By (**M2**), we have $d(a, a) = 0$. Hence we obtain $d(a, b) \geqslant 0$.

To establish (**M4**), we apply (**M1**) to the points a, b, a of X and obtain

$$d(a, a) + d(b, a) \geqslant d(a, b).$$

Because $d(a, a) = 0$, the inequality given above implies $d(b, a) \geqslant d(a, b)$. Similarly, we can prove $d(a, b) \geqslant d(b, a)$. Hence we obtain (**M4**).‖

By a *metric space*, we mean a set X furnished with a metric

$$d : X^2 \to R.$$

EXAMPLES OF METRIC SPACES

(**1**) *The Euclidean n-space R^n.* For the Cartesian power $X = R^n$ of the real line R, we defined in (IV, §1) a function $d : X^2 \to R$ by taking

$$d(a, b) = \| a - b \| = \sqrt{\sum_{i=1}^{n} (a_i - b_i)^2}$$

for any two points $a = (a_1, \ldots, a_n)$ and $b = (b_1, \ldots, b_n)$ in $X = R^n$. Then (**M1**) is a direct consequence of (IV, 1.10) and (IV, 1.11) while (**M2**) is obvious. Hence d is a metric in R^n and makes R^n a metric space. In the special case $n = 1$, the real line R is a metric space with its metric $d : R^2 \to R$ defined by

$$d(a, b) = | a - b |$$

for any two real numbers a and b, where $| x |$ denotes the absolute value of the real number x.

(**2**) *The Hilbert space H.* Let H denote the set of all sequences

$$x = (x_1, x_2, x_3, \ldots)$$

of real numbers such that Σx^2 is a convergent series. The real number x_i is called the ith *coordinate* of the point x. Consider any two points a and b of H with their ith coordinates denoted by a_i and b_i, respectively. For any two real numbers, the Schwarz inequality (IV, 1.5) implies

$$\sum_{i=m}^{n} (\alpha a_i + \beta b_i)^2 \leqslant \alpha^2 \sum_{i=m}^{n} a_i^2 + 2 | \alpha\beta | \left(\sqrt{\sum_{i=m}^{n} a_i^2} \right)\left(\sqrt{\sum_{i=m}^{n} b_i^2} \right) + \beta^2 \sum_{i=m}^{n} b_i^2$$

for any two positive integers m and n with $m < n$. Hence the sequence

$$\alpha a + \beta b = (\alpha a_1 + \beta b_1, \alpha a_2 + \beta b_2, \ldots)$$

is a point in H. In particular, if we take $\alpha = 1$ and $\beta = -1$, it follows that $\Sigma(a_i - b_i)^2$ is a convergent series. Therefore we may define a function $d:H^2 \to R$ by taking

$$d(a, b) = \sqrt{\sum_{i=1}^{\infty} (a_i - b_i)^2}$$

for all points a and b of H. For any three points a, b, c of H, we have

$$d(a, c) + d(b, c) \geqslant \sqrt{\sum_{i=1}^{n} (a_i - c_i)^2} + \sqrt{\sum_{i=1}^{n} (b_i - c_i)^2} \geqslant \sqrt{\sum_{i=1}^{n} (a_i - b_i)^2}$$

because of the condition (**M1**) for the Euclidean metric in R^n. Since this is true for all positive integers n, we obtain

$$d(a, c) + d(b, c) \geqslant d(a, b).$$

Hence d satisfies (**M1**). Since d clearly satisfies (**M2**), it follows that d is a metric in H. This metric space H is called the *Hilbert space.*

(**3**) *The discrete metric space X.* Let X denote an arbitrarily given set. Define a function $d:X^2 \to R$ by taking

$$d(a, b) = \begin{cases} 0 & \text{(if } a = b), \\ 1 & \text{(if } a \neq b), \end{cases}$$

for any two points a and b in X. To verify (**M1**), let a, b, c denote any three points in X. If $a = b$, then $d(a, b) = 0$ and hence we have

$$d(a, c) + d(b, c) \geqslant 0 = d(a, b).$$

If $a \neq b$ holds, then we must have either $a \neq c$ or $b \neq c$. Hence, in this case, we obtain

$$d(a, c) + d(b, c) \geqslant 1 = d(a, b).$$

Therefore d satisfies (**M1**). Since d clearly satisfies (**M2**), it follows that d is a metric in X. This metric space is called the *discrete metric space X.*

This last example shows that every set can be the underlying set of a metric space.

Throughout the remainder of the section, let X denote an arbitrarily given metric space with

$$d:X^2 \to R$$

denoting its metric.

For an arbitrary point p of X and any given positive real number δ, the subset

$$B_\delta(p) = \{x \in X \mid d(p, x) < \delta\}$$

of X is said to be the *open ball with p as center and δ as radius*. Frequently, $B_\delta(p)$ will be called the *δ-neighborhood* of p in X.

Now let us consider a set E in X and a point p of X.

The point p is said to be an *interior point* of the set E iff there exists a positive real number δ such that E contains the δ-neighborhood $B_\delta(p)$ of p in X. The point p is said to be an *exterior point* of the set E iff there exists a positive real number δ such that $B_\delta(p)$ contains no point of E. Finally, the point p is said to be a *boundary point*, or *frontier point*, of E iff, for every positive real number δ, $B_\delta(p)$ contains at least one point in E and at least one point not in E.

The set $\text{Int}(E)$ of all interior points of E is called the *interior* of E. The set $\text{Ext}(E)$ of all exterior points of E is called the *exterior* of E. The set $\partial(E)$ of all boundary points of E is called the *boundary*, or *frontier*, of the set E in the space X. Obviously, we have

$$\text{Int}(E) \subset E,$$
$$\text{Ext}(E) \subset X \backslash E;$$

and a boundary point of E may be in E or may not be in E.

A set E in X is said to be *open* iff every point of E is an interior point of E. In other words, E is an open set of X iff

$$\text{Int}(E) = E.$$

The following proposition is obvious.

PROPOSITION 1.2. *A set E in X is open iff it contains none of its boundary points; in symbols,*

$$E \cap \partial(E) = \square.$$

Let τ denote the collection of all open sets of the metric space X. Frequently, τ is called the *topology* of X.

THEOREM 1.3. *The topology τ of an arbitrary metric space X has the following four properties:*

(**OS1**) *The empty set $\square$ is open.*

(**OS2**) *The set X itself is open.*

(**OS3**) *The union of any family of open sets is open.*

(**OS4**) *The intersection of any two (and hence of any finite number of) open sets is open.*

Proof. To prove (**OS1**), we observe that $\square$ contains no point and hence none of its boundary points. By (1.2), this implies that $\square$ is open.

To prove (**OS2**), we observe that, for every $p \in X$ and any positive real number δ, X contains $B_\delta(p)$. This implies that every point p of X is an interior point of X. According to the definition, this proves that X is open.

To prove (**OS3**), consider any collection

$$\mathfrak{C} = \{\, U_\mu \mid \mu \in M \,\}$$

of open sets of X and let U denote the union of all open sets U_μ in $\mathfrak{C}$. Let p denote an arbitrary point of U. By the definition of union, there exists a $\mu \in M$ with $p \in U_\mu$. Since U_μ is an open set of X, p is an interior point of U_μ and hence there exists a positive real number δ with

$$B_\delta(p) \subset U_\mu \subset U.$$

This implies that p is an interior point of U. Since p is an arbitrary point of U, it follows that U is an open set of X.

To prove (**OS4**), let U and V be any two open sets of X and let p denote an arbitrary point (if any) of $U \cap V$. Since p is an interior point of U, there exists a positive real number ξ satisfying

$$B_\xi(p) \subset U.$$

Similarly, there exists a positive real number η satisfying

$$B_\eta(p) \subset V.$$

Let δ denote the smaller of the two positive real numbers ξ and η. Then we have

$$B_\delta(p) \subset U \cap V.$$

This implies that p is an interior point of $U \cap V$. Since p is any point of $U \cap V$, it follows that $U \cap V$ is an open set of X.‖

PROPOSITION 1.4.   *For every point p of X and any positive real number δ, $B_\delta(p)$ is an open set of X.*

Proof.   Let q denote an arbitrary point of $B_\delta(p)$, and consider the distance

$$\gamma = d(p, q).$$

According to the definition of $B_\delta(p)$, we have $\gamma < \delta$. Let

$$\beta = \delta - \gamma > 0.$$

For an arbitrary point $x \in B_\beta(q)$, it follows from (**M1**) and (**M4**) that we have

$$d(p, x) \leqslant d(p, q) + d(q, x) < \gamma + \beta = \delta.$$

This implies

$$B_\beta(q) \subset B_\delta(p).$$

Hence q is an interior point of $B_\delta(p)$. Since q is an arbitrary point of $B_\delta(p)$, it follows that $B_\delta(p)$ is an open set of X.$\|$

PROPOSITION 1.5. *Every nonempty open set of X is a union of open balls of X.*

Proof. Let U denote an arbitrary nonempty open set of X. For each point $p \in U$, U contains an open ball U_p with p as center and with some positive real number δ_p as radius. Then we have

$$U = \bigcup_{p \in U} U_p.$$

This proves (1.5).$\|$

PROPOSITION 1.6. *The interior $\mathrm{Int}(E)$ of a set E in X is the largest open set of X contained in E.*

Proof. Let U denote an arbitrary open set of X contained in E. We will show that $U \subset \mathrm{Int}(E)$. For this purpose, let p be any point in U. By definition of open sets, p is an interior point of U. Hence there exists a positive real number δ satisfying

$$B_\delta(p) \subset U \subset E.$$

This implies that p is an interior point of E. Since p is any point of U, it follows that we have

$$U \subset \mathrm{Int}(E).$$

Next, for each interior point p of E, choose an open ball U_p with p as center and some positive real number δ_p as radius such that

$$U_p \subset E.$$

Let U denote the union of the open balls U_p for all interior points p of E. This implies

$$\mathrm{Int}(E) \subset U \subset E.$$

By (1.4) and **(OS3)** in (1.3), U is an open set of X. Hence it follows from the first part of the proof that we have

$$U \subset \mathrm{Int}(E).$$

Consequently, $\mathrm{Int}(E) = U$ is an open set of X.

Combining both parts of the proof, we conclude that $\mathrm{Int}(E)$ is open and contains every open set of X which is contained in E.$\|$

On the other extreme, we introduce the notion of closed sets of X as follows.

A set E in X is said to be *closed* iff E contains all of its boundary points; in symbols,

$$\partial(E) \subset E.$$

Note that a set which contains some but not all of its boundary points is neither open nor closed. On the other hand, if a set has no boundary point in X, then it is both open and closed.

PROPOSITION 1.7.   *A set E in X is closed iff its complement $X \backslash E$ is open.*

Proof.   It follows directly from the definition of boundary points that

$$\partial(E) = \partial(X \backslash E).$$

To prove the necessity, let us assume that E is closed. According to definition, we have $\partial(E) \subset E$. This implies that $X \backslash E$ contains none of its boundary points. Hence $X \backslash E$ is open according to (1.2).

To prove the sufficiency, let us assume that $X \backslash E$ is open. By (1.2), $\partial(X \backslash E)$ must be contained in E. Hence, $\partial(E) \subset E$ and E is closed by definition.‖

The preceding proposition establishes duality between the closed sets and open sets of X by means of taking complements. Because of this duality, one can easily deduce the properties of closed sets dual to those of open sets, and vice versa. For example, the following proposition can be established in this way.

PROPOSITION 1.8.   *The closed sets of X satisfy the following four conditions:*

(**CS1**)   *The empty set $\square$ is closed.*
(**CS2**)   *The set X itself is closed.*
(**CS3**)   *The intersection of any collection of closed sets is closed.*
(**CS4**)   *The union of any two (and hence of any finite number of) closed sets is closed.*

PROPOSITION 1.9.   *Every singleton in X is closed.*

Proof.   Let E denote an arbitrary singleton in X. Then, by definition, E consists of a single point of X, say

$$E = \{p\}.$$

According to (1.7), it suffices to prove that its complement $X \backslash E$ is open. For this purpose, let q denote an arbitrary point in $X \backslash E$. Let

$$\delta = d(p, q).$$

Since $p \neq q$, it follows from (**M2**) and (**M3**) that δ is a positive real number. Then $B_\delta(q)$ is an open ball which does not contain p. This implies

$$B_\delta(q) \subset X \backslash E$$

and hence q is an interior point of $X \backslash E$. Since q is any point of $X \backslash E$, it follows that $X \backslash E$ is open. $\|$

The following corollary is a direct consequence of (1.9) and (**CS4**).

COROLLARY 1.10. *Every finite set in X is closed.*

By the *closure* of a set E in X, we mean the set

$$\mathrm{Cl}(E) = E \cup \partial(E) = \mathrm{Int}(E) \cup \partial(E).$$

Dual to (1.6), we will establish the following proposition.

PROPOSITION 1.11. *The closure $\mathrm{Cl}(E)$ of a set E in X is the smallest closed set of X which contains E.*

Proof. To prove that $\mathrm{Cl}(E)$ is closed, let us consider its complement

$$X \backslash \mathrm{Cl}(E) = \mathrm{Ext}(E).$$

By the definition, one can easily see that

$$\mathrm{Ext}(E) = \mathrm{Int}(X \backslash E).$$

It follows from (1.6) that $X \backslash \mathrm{Cl}(E)$ is open. According to (1.7), this implies that $\mathrm{Cl}(E)$ is a closed set.

Next, let F denote an arbitrary closed set containing E. Then, by (1.7), $X \backslash F$ is an open set contained in $X \backslash E$. According to (1.6), we obtain

$$X \backslash F \subset \mathrm{Int}(X \backslash E) = \mathrm{Ext}(E).$$

This implies

$$\mathrm{Cl}(E) = X \backslash \mathrm{Ext}(E) \subset F.$$

Combining both parts of the proof, we conclude that $\mathrm{Cl}(E)$ is closed and is contained in every closed set of X which contains E. $\|$

The duality between $\mathrm{Int}(E)$ and $\mathrm{Cl}(E)$ is clarified by the following proposition which is a direct consequence of (1.6) and (1.11).

PROPOSITION 1.12. *For an arbitrary set E in X, we have:*

(i) *E is open iff $\mathrm{Int}(E) = E$;*
(ii) *E is closed iff $\mathrm{Cl}(E) = E$.*

A characterization of the points in $\mathrm{Cl}(E)$ is given by the following proposition.

PROPOSITION 1.13.   *A point p of X is in the closure $\mathrm{Cl}(E)$ of a set $E \subset X$ iff, for every positive real number δ, $B_\delta(p)$ meets the set E.*

Proof. Necessity.   Assume that p is in $\mathrm{Cl}(E)$. Since

$$\mathrm{Cl}(E) = E \cup \partial(E),$$

we must have $p \in E$ or $p \in \partial(E)$. If $p \in E$, then $B_\delta(p) \cap E$ contains the point p; if $p \in \partial(E)$, then it follows from the definition of $\partial(E)$ that $B_\delta(p)$ contains at least one point of E. Hence

$$B_\delta(p) \cap E \neq \square$$

holds for both cases and the necessity is established.

Sufficiency.   Assume that, for every positive real number δ, $B_\delta(p)$ meets E. We have to prove

$$p \in \mathrm{Cl}(E) = E \cup \partial(E).$$

This is obvious if $p \in E$. Hence we may assume $p \notin E$. Then, for every positive real δ, $B_\delta(p)$ also contains a point not in E. By definition of $\partial(E)$, this implies

$$p \in \partial(E) \subset \mathrm{Cl}(E)$$

and proves the sufficiency.‖

If p is a point in $\mathrm{Cl}(E)$ but not in E, then, for every positive real number δ, $B_\delta(p)$ contains at least one point of E other than p. This suggests the following definition.

A point p of X is said to be an *accumulation point* (or *cluster point*, or *limit point*) of a set E in X iff, for every positive real number δ, $B_\delta(p)$ contains at least one point of E other than p. The set E' of all accumulation points of E in X is called the *derived set* of E in X. Then, we have

$$\mathrm{Cl}(E) = E \cup E'.$$

It is obvious that a set E in X is closed iff it contains all of its accumulation points.

EXERCISES

1A.   For an arbitrary metric d in any given set X, prove

$$|\, d(a,\, c) - d(b,\, c)\,| \leqslant d(a,\, b)$$
$$d(x_1,\, x_n) \leqslant \sum_{i=1}^{n-1} d(x_i,\, x_{i+1})$$

for arbitrary points a, b, c, x_1, x_2, ..., x_n in the set X.

1B. For any subset A of a given set X, prove that the restriction

$$e = d \mid A^2 : A^2 \to R$$

of every metric $d : X^2 \to R$ is a metric in A. The metric space (A, e) is called a *subspace* of the metric space (X, d).

1C. Let A and B be any two sets in a metric space X. Prove the following properties of the operation of forming the interior of a set:

   (a) $\text{Int}[\text{Int}(A)] = \text{Int}(A)$;
   (b) $\text{Int}[A \cup B] \supset \text{Int}(A) \cup \text{Int}(B)$;
   (c) $\text{Int}[A \cap B] = \text{Int}(A) \cap \text{Int}(B)$.

In case (b), give an example of two sets A and B in the real line R such that $\text{Int}(A \cup B)$ is not equal to $\text{Int}(A) \cup \text{Int}(B)$.

1D. Let A and B be any two sets in a metric space X. Prove the following properties of the operation of forming the closure of a set:

   (a) $\text{Cl}[\text{Cl}(A)] = \text{Cl}(A)$;
   (b) $\text{Cl}[A \cup B] = \text{Cl}(A) \cup \text{Cl}(B)$;
   (c) $\text{Cl}[A \cap B] \subset \text{Cl}(A) \cap \text{Cl}(B)$.

In case (c), give an example of two sets A and B in the real line R such that $\text{Cl}(A \cap B)$ is not equal to $\text{Cl}(A) \cap \text{Cl}(B)$.

1E. For an arbitrary set E in a metric space X, establish the following relations between interior and closure:

   (a) $\text{Int}(X \backslash E) = X \backslash \text{Cl}(E)$;
   (b) $\text{Cl}(X \backslash E) = X \backslash \text{Int}(E)$.

1F. Let A and B be any two sets in a metric space X. Prove that

$$\partial(A \cup B) \subset \partial(A) \cup \partial(B),$$

and give an example to show that $\partial(A \cup B)$ may be different from $\partial(A) \cup \partial(B)$.

1G. For an arbitrary set E in a metric space X, prove that

$$\partial(E) = \text{Cl}(E) \cap \text{Cl}(X \backslash E).$$

1H. A set E in a metric space X is said to be *dense* iff $\text{Cl}(E) = X$. Let E denote a dense subset of X and let U be an open subset of X. Prove that $U \subset \text{Cl}(E \cap U)$.

2. CONVERGENCE OF SEQUENCES

Throughout the present section, let X be an arbitrarily given metric space with

$$d:X^2 \to R$$

denoting its distance function.

Let N denote the set of all natural numbers.

By a *sequence* in X, we mean a function

$$\phi:N \to X.$$

For every natural number $n \in N$, the point

$$x_n = \phi(n) \in X$$

is called the nth *term* of the sequence ϕ. The sequence ϕ is often denoted by

$$\phi = \{x_1, x_2, \ldots, x_n, \ldots\}.$$

Let $\phi:N \to X$ denote any given sequence in X and let U be an arbitrary subset of X. The sequence ϕ is said to be *in* U iff

$$\phi(N) \subset U$$

holds. The sequence ϕ is said to be *eventually in* U iff there exists a natural number k such that

$$\phi(n) \in U$$

holds for every natural number $n \geq k$. The sequence ϕ is said to be *frequently in* U iff, for every natural number n, there exists a natural number $k \geq n$ satisfying

$$\phi(k) \in U.$$

The sequence $\phi:N \to X$ is said to *converge* to a point $p \in X$ iff, for every positive real number δ, ϕ is eventually in the open ball B_δ. In other words, ϕ *converges* to the point $p \in X$ iff, for every positive real number δ, there exists a natural number k_δ such that

$$d[p, \phi(n)] < \delta$$

holds for every natural number $n \geq k_\delta$. Here, we emphasize the fact that, in general, the natural number k_δ depends on the positive real number δ.

THEOREM 2.1. *A sequence* $\phi:N \to X$ *in a metric space* X *can converge to at most one point of* X.

Proof. Assume that $\phi:N \to X$ is a sequence which converges to two distinct points p and q of the metric space X. Let

$$\delta = \tfrac{1}{2}d(p, q).$$

By (**M2**) and (**M3**) in §1, we have $\delta > 0$. Since ϕ converges to the point p, there exists a natural number i such that

$$d[p, \phi(n)] < \delta$$

holds for every natural number $n \geqslant i$. On the other hand, since ϕ converges to the point q, there exists a natural number j such that

$$d[q, \phi(n)] < \delta$$

holds for every natural number $n \geqslant j$. Let n denote a natural number which satisfies both $n \geqslant i$ and $n \geqslant j$. Then we obtain

$$d(p, q) \leqslant d[p, \phi(n)] + d[q, \phi(n)] < \delta + \delta = d(p, q)$$

because of the triangle inequality (**M1**). This contradiction proves (2.1).$\|$

If a sequence $\phi : \mathcal{N} \to X$ in a metric space X converges to a point $p \, \epsilon \, X$, then it follows from (2.1) that the point p is uniquely determined by the sequence ϕ and is said to be the *limit* of the sequence ϕ; in symbols,

$$\lim (\phi) = p.$$

In case the sequence ϕ is given by its terms $\{x_1, x_2, \ldots, x_n, \ldots\}$, its limit is often denoted by the symbol

$$\lim_{n \to \infty} x_n.$$

The convergence of sequences in a metric space X characterizes the topology of X. Precisely, we have the following theorem.

THEOREM 2.2. *A set U in a metric space X is open iff no sequence in $X \setminus U$ can converge to a point of U.*

Proof. Necessity. Assume that U is open and that $\phi : \mathcal{N} \to X$ is a sequence which converges to a point $p \, \epsilon \, U$. Since U is open, there exists a positive real number δ satisfying

$$B_\delta(p) \subset U.$$

Since ϕ converges to the point p, there exists a natural number k such that

$$\phi(n) \, \epsilon \, B_\delta(p) \subset U$$

holds for every natural number $n \geqslant k$. This implies that ϕ can never be in $X \setminus U$.

Sufficiency. Assume that U is not open. Then there exists a point $p \, \epsilon \, U$ which is a boundary point of U by (1.2). Define a sequence

$$\phi : \mathcal{N} \to X$$

as follows. Let $n \, \epsilon \, \mathcal{N}$ be arbitrarily given. Since p is a boundary point of U, it follows that the open ball $B_\delta(p)$ with $\delta = n^{-1}$ meets $X \backslash U$. Select a point

$$\phi(n) \, \epsilon \, B_\delta(p) \cap (X \backslash U).$$

The assignment $n \to \phi(n)$ for each $n \, \epsilon \, \mathcal{N}$ defines a sequence ϕ in $X \backslash U$ which obviously converges to the point p. Hence the condition cannot hold.‖

COROLLARY 2.3. *A set E in a metric space X is closed iff no sequence in E can converge to a point of $X \backslash E$.*

PROPOSITION 2.4. *A point p of a metric space belongs to the closure $\mathrm{Cl}(E)$ of a set E in X iff there exists a sequence ϕ in E which converges to p.*

Proof. *Necessity.* Assume that $p \, \epsilon \, \mathrm{Cl}(E)$. Then, for every natural number n, the open ball $B_{n^{-1}}(p)$ meets the set E and hence we may select a point

$$\phi(n) \, \epsilon \, E \cap B_{n^{-1}}(p).$$

The assignment $n \to \phi(n)$ for each $n \, \epsilon \, \mathcal{N}$ defines a sequence ϕ in E which clearly converges to the point p.

Sufficiency. Let $\phi : \mathcal{N} \to X$ denote a sequence in E which converges to p. Let δ be an arbitrary positive real number. Since ϕ converges to p, there exists a natural number k such that

$$\phi(n) \, \epsilon \, B_\delta(p)$$

holds for every natural number $n \geqslant k$. In particular, we have

$$E \cap B_\delta(p) \neq \square$$

for every positive real number δ. Hence, p is in $\mathrm{Cl}(E)$.‖

PROPOSITION 2.5. *A point p of a metric space X is an accumulation point of a set E in X iff there exists a sequence ϕ in $E \backslash \{p\}$ which converges to p.*

Proof. *Necessity.* Let p be any accumulation point of E. Then, for every natural number n, the open ball $B_{n^{-1}}(p)$ contains at least one point of E other than p and hence we may select a point

$$\phi(n) \, \epsilon \, (E \backslash \{p\}) \cap B_{n^{-1}}(p).$$

The assignment $n \to \phi(n)$ for each $n \, \epsilon \, \mathcal{N}$ defines a sequence ϕ in $E \backslash \{p\}$ which clearly converges to the point p.

Sufficiency. Let $\phi : \mathcal{N} \to X$ denote a sequence in $E \backslash \{p\}$ which converges to p. Let δ be an arbitrary positive real number. Since ϕ converges to p, there exists a natural number k such that

$$\phi(n) \, \epsilon \, B_\delta(p)$$

holds for every natural number $n \geqslant k$. In particular, we have

$$(E \backslash \{p\}) \cap B_\delta(p) \neq \square$$

for every positive real number δ. Hence p is an accumulation point of E. ‖

PROPOSITION 2.6. *A point p of a metric space X is a boundary point of a set E in X iff there exists a sequence ϕ in E and a sequence ψ in $X \backslash E$ both converging to p.*

Proof. Because of $\partial(E) = \mathrm{Cl}(E) \cap \mathrm{Cl}(X \backslash E)$, this proposition is a direct consequence of (2.4). ‖

A function $\lambda : \mathcal{N} \to \mathcal{N}$ is said to be *strictly increasing* iff, for any two natural numbers i and j, $i < j$ implies

$$\lambda(i) < \lambda(j).$$

Consequently, every strictly increasing function $\lambda : \mathcal{N} \to \mathcal{N}$ is injective.

By a *subsequence* of a sequence $\phi : \mathcal{N} \to X$, we mean a sequence $\psi : \mathcal{N} \to X$ such that there exists a strictly increasing function $\lambda : \mathcal{N} \to \mathcal{N}$ with

$$\psi = \phi \circ \lambda.$$

For example, if $\lambda : \mathcal{N} \to \mathcal{N}$ is defined by $\lambda(n) = 2n$ for every $n \in \mathcal{N}$, the subsequence $\psi = \phi \circ \lambda$ of the sequence ϕ is called the *subsequence of even terms* of ϕ; in fact, if

$$\phi = \{x_1, x_2, \ldots, x_n, \ldots\},$$

then we have

$$\psi = \phi \circ \lambda = \{x_2, x_4, \ldots, x_{2n}, \ldots\}.$$

Now, let us consider a given sequence

$$\phi : \mathcal{N} \to X$$

in a metric space X. A point $p \in X$ is called a *cluster point* of the sequence ϕ iff, for every positive real number δ, ϕ is frequently in $B_\delta(p)$. In other words, p is a cluster point of ϕ iff, for every positive real number δ and every natural number k, there exists a natural number n satisfying $n \geqslant k$ and

$$d[p, \phi(n)] < \delta.$$

PROPOSITION 2.7. *A point p in a metric space X is a cluster point of a sequence $\phi : \mathcal{N} \to X$ iff there exists a subsequence $\psi : \mathcal{N} \to X$ of ϕ which converges to p.*

Proof. Necessity. Let p be a cluster point of a sequence $\phi : \mathcal{N} \to X$. Define a strictly increasing function

$$\lambda : \mathcal{N} \to \mathcal{N}$$

as follows. Since p is a cluster point of ϕ, there exists a natural number $\lambda(1) \in \mathcal{N}$ such that

$$d\{p, \phi[\lambda(1)]\} < 1.$$

To complete the inductive construction of λ, let $n > 1$ denote an arbitrary natural number and assume that we have already defined $\lambda(n - 1)$. Since p is a cluster point of ϕ, there exists a natural number $\lambda(n)$ satisfying $\lambda(n) \geqslant \lambda(n - 1) + 1$ and

$$d\{p, \phi[\lambda(n)]\} < n^{-1}.$$

This completes the construction of the strictly increasing function λ. Thus we obtain a subsequence

$$\psi = \phi \circ \lambda : \mathcal{N} \to X$$

of ϕ. Since

$$d[p, \psi(n)] = d\{p, \phi[\lambda(n)]\} < n^{-1}$$

holds for every $n \in \mathcal{N}$, ψ obviously converges to the point p.

Sufficiency. Assume that the sequence ϕ has a subsequence ψ which converges to p. To prove that p is a cluster point of ϕ, let δ denote any positive real number and k any natural number. Since ψ is a subsequence of ϕ, there exists a strictly increasing function $\lambda : \mathcal{N} \to \mathcal{N}$ satisfying

$$\psi = \phi \circ \lambda : \mathcal{N} \to X.$$

Since λ is strictly increasing, there exists a natural number m such that $\lambda(m) \geqslant k$ holds. Since ψ converges to p, there exists a natural number n satisfying $n \geqslant m$ and

$$d[p, \psi(n)] < \delta.$$

Since λ is strictly increasing, we have

$$\lambda(n) \geqslant \lambda(m) \geqslant k.$$

On the other hand, we have

$$d\{p, \phi[\lambda(n)]\} = d[p, \psi(n)] < \delta.$$

This proves that p is a cluster point of the sequence ϕ. $\|$

A sequence $\phi : \mathcal{N} \to X$ in a metric space X is said to be *convergent* iff it converges to some point of X. As a necessary condition for convergent sequences, we have the following proposition.

PROPOSITION 2.8. *Every convergent sequence $\phi : \mathcal{N} \to X$ in a metric space X satisfies Cauchy's condition that, for every positive real number δ, there exists a natural number k_δ such that*

$$d[\phi(i), \phi(j)] < \delta$$

holds for every $i \geqslant k_\delta$ and $j \geqslant k_\delta$.

Proof. By definition of convergent sequences, there exists a point p of X such that ϕ converges to p. Then there exists a natural number k_δ such that

$$d[p, \phi(n)] < \delta/2$$

holds for every natural number $n \geqslant k_\delta$. Hence, for every $i \geqslant k_\delta$ and every $j \geqslant k_\delta$, we obtain

$$d[\phi(i), \phi(j)] \leqslant d[p, \phi(i)] + d[p, \phi(j)] < \frac{\delta}{2} + \frac{\delta}{2} = \delta.$$

This proves (2.8).‖

By a *fundamental sequence* (or *Cauchy sequence*) in a metric space X, we mean a sequence $\phi:N \to X$ which satisfies Cauchy's condition stated in (2.8).

By (2.8), every convergent sequence in a metric space is a fundamental sequence. But the converse is not always true. For example, let X denote the subspace of the real line R which consists of all rational numbers. Then, as studied in (II, §4), there are infinitely many fundamental sequences in X which are not convergent.

A metric space X is said to be *complete* iff every fundamental sequence in X is convergent. For example, the real line R is complete in view of (II, Exercise 4F).

If a given metric space X is not complete, then the construction of real numbers given in (II, §4) can be generalized to construct a complete metric space X^* containing X as a subspace which is *dense* in X; that is,

$$\text{Cl}(X) = X^*.$$

Interested readers will be able to find the details in the author's book *Introduction to General Topology*.

EXERCISES

2A. For each $i = 1, 2, \ldots, n$, let $p_i:R^n \to R$ denote the orthogonal projection of the Euclidean n-space R^n onto its ith coordinate axis defined by $p_i(x) = x_i$ for every point $x = (x_1, \ldots, x_n)$ of R^n. Prove that a sequence $\phi:N \to R^n$ is convergent iff the n sequences

$$\phi_i = p_i \circ \phi:N \to R \qquad (i = 1, 2, \ldots, n)$$

of real numbers are convergent.

2B. Prove that Euclidean n-space R^n and the Hilbert space H are complete.

2C. Prove that every closed subspace of a complete metric space is complete.

3. CONTINUITY OF FUNCTIONS

Throughout the present section, let X and Y denote arbitrary metric spaces with metrics

$$d:X^2 \to R, \qquad e:Y^2 \to R,$$

respectively, and consider any function

$$f:X \to Y.$$

We will first introduce the notion of *uniform continuity* as follows.

The function $f:X \to Y$ is said to be *uniformly continuous* iff, for every positive real number ε, there exists a positive real number δ such that

$$e[f(a), f(b)] < \varepsilon$$

holds for every pair (a, b) of points of X satisfying

$$d(a, b) < \delta.$$

For examples of uniformly continuous functions, we have the following propositions.

PROPOSITION 3.1.   *Every constant function $f:X \to Y$ from a metric space X to a metric space Y is uniformly continuous.*

Proof.   Let ε denote any given positive number. Let (a, b) be any pair of points in X. Since f is a constant function, we have

$$f(a) = f(b)$$

and hence

$$e[f(a), f(b)] = 0 < \varepsilon$$

according to Condition (**M2**) for the metric e. Hence the condition in the definition of uniform continuity is satisfied for any arbitrarily chosen positive real number δ. In particular, f is uniformly continuous.‖

In general, the positive real number δ in the definition of uniform continuity depends on the given positive real number ε as well as the given function f.

The function $f:X \to Y$ is said to be *isometric* iff

$$e[f(a), f(b)] = d(a, b)$$

holds for every pair (a, b) of points of X. In particular, if

$$X \subset Y, \qquad d = e \mid X^2,$$

then the inclusion function $i:X \to Y$ is isometric.

PROPOSITION 3.2. *Every isometric function $f:X \to Y$ from a metric space X to a metric space Y is injective and uniformly continuous.*

Proof. To prove that $f:X \to Y$ is injective, let a and b denote any two points of X with

$$f(a) = f(b).$$

Since f is isometric, we obtain

$$d(a, b) = e[f(a), f(b)] = 0$$

according to Condition (**M2**) for the metric e. By (**M2**) for the metric d, this implies $a = b$. Hence f is injective.

To establish the uniform continuity of f, let ε denote an arbitrarily given positive real number. Take $\delta = \varepsilon$. Then

$$e[f(a), f(b)] < \varepsilon$$

holds for every pair (a, b) of points of X satisfying $d(a, b) < \delta$. Hence, by definition, f is uniformly continuous. $\|$

The function $f:X \to Y$ is said to be *submetric* iff

$$e[f(a), f(b)] \leqslant d(a, b)$$

holds for every pair (a, b) of points of X. In particular, constant functions and isometric functions are submetric.

The proof of the following proposition is exactly the same as the second part of the preceding proof.

PROPOSITION 3.3. *Every submetric function $f:X \to Y$ from a metric space X to a metric space Y is uniformly continuous.*

Submetric functions are special cases of the functions satisfying the *uniform Lipschitz condition* defined as follows.

The function $f:X \to Y$ is said to *satisfy the uniform Lipschitz condition* iff there exists a positive real number M such that

$$e[f(a), f(b)] \leqslant Md(a, b)$$

holds for every pair (a, b) of points of X. In particular, if $f:X \to Y$ is submetric, the f satisfies the uniform Lipschitz condition with $M = 1$.

PROPOSITION 3.4. *If $f:X \to Y$ satisfies the uniform Lipschitz condition, then f is uniformly continuous.*

Proof. Assume that $f:X \to Y$ satisfies the uniform Lipschitz condition. Then there exists a positive real number M such that

$$e[f(a), f(b)] \leqslant Md(a, b)$$

holds for every pair (a, b) of points of X. To prove the uniform continuity of f, let ε denote an arbitrarily given positive real number. Take $\delta = \varepsilon/M$. Then

$$e[f(a), f(b)] \leqslant Md(a, b) < M\delta = \varepsilon$$

holds for every pair (a, b) of points of X satisfying $d(a, b) < \delta$. Hence, by definition, f is uniformly continuous.$\|$

Now let us introduce the notion of *continuity* at a given point x_0 of the metric space X.

The function $f : X \to Y$ is said to be *continuous at a point* $x_0 \in X$ iff, for every given positive real number ε, there exists a positive real number δ such that

$$e[f(x_0), f(x)] < \varepsilon$$

holds for every point x of X satisfying

$$d(x_0, x) < \delta.$$

The function $f : X \to Y$ is said to be *continuous* iff it is continuous at every point of X.

Obviously, every uniformly continuous function is continuous, but the converse is not always true. If a function

$$f : X \to Y$$

is continuous, then, for an arbitrarily given positive real number ε, there exists a positive real number $\delta(\varepsilon, x_0)$ for every point $x_0 \in X$ such that

$$e[f(x), f(x_0)] < \varepsilon$$

holds for every point x of X satisfying

$$d(x_0, x) < \delta(\varepsilon, x_0).$$

In general, the positive real number $\delta(\varepsilon, x_0)$ depends not only on the given positive real number ε but also on the point x_0. It might be impossible to find a positive real number δ satisfying

$$\delta \leqslant \delta(\varepsilon, x_0)$$

for all $x_0 \in X$. This indicates that f might not be uniformly continuous.

For example, let $X = Y$ denote the subspace of the real line R which consists of all positive real numbers and

$$f : X \to Y$$

denote the function defined by

$$f(x) = 1/x$$

for every $x \in X$. Then f is continuous but not uniformly continuous.

In terms of convergence of sequences, we have a necessary and sufficient condition for continuity as follows.

THEOREM 3.5. *The function $f:X \to Y$ is continuous at $x_0 \in X$ iff, for every sequence $\phi:N \to X$ which converges to x_0, the composition*

$$\psi = f \circ \phi:N \to Y$$

converges to the point $f(x_0) \in Y$.

Proof. Necessity. Assume that $f:X \to Y$ is continuous at x_0 and let $\phi:N \to X$ denote an arbitrary sequence in X which converges to x_0. To prove that the composed sequence

$$\psi = f \circ \phi:N \to Y$$

converges to $f(x_0)$, let ε denote any given positive real number. Since f is continuous at x_0, there exists a positive real number δ such that

$$e[f(x_0), f(x)] < \varepsilon$$

holds for every point $x \in X$ satisfying

$$d(x_0, x) < \delta.$$

Since ϕ converges to x_0, there exists a natural number k such that

$$d[x_0, \phi(n)] < \delta$$

holds for every natural number $n \geqslant k$. Hence we obtain

$$e[f(x_0), \psi(n)] = e\{f(x_0), f[\phi(n)]\} < \varepsilon$$

for every natural number $n \geqslant k$. This proves that ψ converges to $f(x_0)$.

Sufficiency. Assume that f is not continuous at x_0. Then, there exists a positive real number ε such that, for any given positive real number δ, there exists a point $x \in X$ satisfying

$$d(x_0, x) < \delta, \qquad e[f(x_0), f(x)] \geqslant \varepsilon.$$

In particular, for every natural number n, there exists a point $x_n \in X$ satisfying

$$d(x_0, x_n) < n^{-1}, \qquad e[f(x_0), f(x_n)] \geqslant \varepsilon.$$

Define a sequence $\phi:N \to X$ by taking

$$\phi(n) = x_n$$

for every $n \in N$. Since

$$d[x_0, \phi(n)] = d(x_0, x_n) < n^{-1}$$

holds for every $n \in N$, ϕ obviously converges to x_0. On the other hand, the composition

$$\psi = f \circ \phi : N \to Y$$

does not converge to $f(x_0)$ since

$$e[f(x_0), \psi(n)] = e[f(x_0), f(x_n)] \geqslant \varepsilon$$

holds for every $n \in N$. This implies that the condition in (3.5) is not satisfied.‖

In terms of the notions introduced in §1, we have more necessary and sufficient conditions for continuity. In fact, we have the following theorem.

THEOREM 3.6. *If* $f : X \to Y$ *is a function from a metric space* X *into a metric space* Y, *then the following statements are equivalent.*

(**i**)   *The function* $f : X \to Y$ *is continuous.*
(**ii**)   *The inverse image* $f^{-1}(U)$ *of every open set* U *in* Y *is open in* X.
(**iii**)   *The inverse image* $f^{-1}(F)$ *of every closed set* F *in* Y *is closed in* X.
(**iv**) $f[\mathrm{Cl}(A)] \subset \mathrm{Cl}[f(A)]$ *holds for each* $A \subset X$.
(**v**) $f^{-1}[\mathrm{Cl}(B)] \supset \mathrm{Cl}[f^{-1}(B)]$ *holds for each* $B \subset Y$.

Proof. (**i**) $\Rightarrow$ (**ii**). Let U denote any open set in Y. We are going to prove that $f^{-1}(U)$ is open in X. For this purpose, let p denote an arbitrary point in $f^{-1}(U)$. Then $f(p)$ is a point in U. Since U is open, there exists a positive real number ε such that

$$B_\varepsilon(p) \subset U$$

holds. Since f is continuous, there exists a positive real number δ such that

$$f[B_\delta(p)] \subset B_\varepsilon(p).$$

It follows that $B_\delta(p)$ is contained in $f^{-1}(U)$. Since p is any point of $f^{-1}(U)$, this implies that $f^{-1}(U)$ is open in X.

(**ii**) $\Rightarrow$ (**iii**). Let F denote any closed set in Y. We are going to prove that $f^{-1}(F)$ is closed in X. For this purpose, consider the open set

$$U = Y \backslash F$$

in Y. According to (**ii**), the inverse image $f^{-1}(U)$ is open in X. By (c) of (I, 5.2), we have

$$f^{-1}(F) = f^{-1}(Y \backslash U) = X \backslash f^{-1}(U).$$

This implies that $f^{-1}(F)$ is closed in X.

(iii) $\Rightarrow$ (iv). Let A be an arbitrary set in X. Then $\mathrm{Cl}[f(A)]$ is a closed set in Y. By (iii), $f^{-1}\{\mathrm{Cl}[f(A)]\}$ is a closed set in X. Obviously, we have

$$A \subset f^{-1}\{\mathrm{Cl}[f(A)]\}.$$

By (1.11), $\mathrm{Cl}(A)$ is the smallest closed set in X containing A. This implies

$$\mathrm{Cl}(A) \subset f^{-1}\{\mathrm{Cl}[f(A)]\}.$$

Consequently, we obtain

$$f[\mathrm{Cl}(A)] \subset \mathrm{Cl}[f(A)].$$

(iv) $\Rightarrow$ (v). Let B be an arbitrary set in Y and let $A = f^{-1}(B)$. Then, by (iv), we have

$$f[\mathrm{Cl}(A)] \subset \mathrm{Cl}[f(A)] \subset \mathrm{Cl}(B).$$

This implies

$$\mathrm{Cl}(A) \subset f^{-1}[\mathrm{Cl}(B)].$$

Consequently, we obtain

$$f^{-1}[\mathrm{Cl}(B)] \supset \mathrm{Cl}[f^{-1}(B)].$$

(v) $\Rightarrow$ (i). Let p be an arbitrary point of X and let ε denote any given positive real number. By (1.4), the set $B_\varepsilon[f(p)]$ is open in Y. Consider the closed set

$$B = Y \backslash B_\varepsilon[f(p)]$$

in Y. According to (v), we have

$$\mathrm{Cl}[f^{-1}(B)] \subset f^{-1}[\mathrm{Cl}(B)] = f^{-1}(B).$$

By (1.11), this implies that $f^{-1}(B)$ is a closed set in X. Hence the set

$$U = X \backslash f^{-1}(B)$$

is open and contains the point p. This implies the existence of a positive real number δ satisfying

$$B_\delta(p) \subset U.$$

Consequently, we obtain

$$f[B_\delta(p)] \subset f(U) \subset B_\varepsilon[f(p)].$$

This proves that f is continuous at the point p. Since p is an arbitrary point of X, f is continuous. ‖

EXERCISES

3A. Let $f:X \to Y$ and $g:Y \to Z$ denote continuous functions of metric spaces. Prove that their composition

$$h = g \circ f:X \to Z$$

is a continuous function. Furthermore, prove that if f and g are uniformly continuous, then so is h.

3B. Let $f:X \to Y$ be a surjective isometric function from a metric space X onto a metric space Y. Prove that f must be bijective and that both f and its inverse $f^{-1}:Y \to X$ are uniformly continuous.

3C. Let E denote any subset of a metric space X. Consider the characteristic function

$$\chi_E:X \to R$$

from X into the real line R defined by

$$\chi_E(x) = \begin{cases} 1 & \text{(if } x \in E), \\ 0 & \text{(if } x \in X \backslash E). \end{cases}$$

Prove that χ_E is continuous at a point $p \in X$ iff p is not a boundary point of E.

3D. By a *sequence of functions from X to Y*, we mean a function

$$\phi:N \to W = \text{Fun}(X, Y)$$

from the set N of all natural numbers to the set

$$W = \text{Fun}(X, Y)$$

of all functions from X to Y. For each natural number $n \in N$,

$$\phi(n) = f_n:X \to Y$$

is a function from X to Y and is called the nth *term* of the sequence ϕ. The sequence ϕ is often denoted by

$$\phi = \{f_1, f_2, \ldots, f_n, \ldots\}.$$

Assume that Y is a metric space. The sequence ϕ is said to *converge* to a function $f:X \to Y$ iff, for every $x \in X$, the sequence

$$\{f_1(x), f_2(x), \ldots, f_n(x), \ldots\}$$

in the metric space Y converges to the point $f(x)$. Prove that ϕ can converge to at most one function from X to Y.

3E. A sequence $\phi = \{f_1, f_2, \ldots, f_n, \ldots\}$ of functions from a set X to a metric space Y is said to *converge uniformly* to a function $f:X \to Y$ iff, for every positive real number ε, there exists a natural number k such that

$$e[f(x), f_n(x)] < \varepsilon$$

holds for every point $x \in X$ and every natural number $n \geqslant k$, where

$$e : \Upsilon^2 \to R$$

denotes the metric in Υ. Assume that both X and Υ are metric spaces. Let

$$\phi = \{f_1, f_2, \ldots, f_n, \ldots\}$$

be a sequence of continuous functions from X to Υ which converges uniformly to a function $f : X \to \Upsilon$. Prove that f is continuous.

4. TOPOLOGICAL SPACES

For a space that does not possess a satisfactory metric, one has to define its topology by other methods. Because of this, we will axiomatize the notion of topology by means of the properties given in (1.3).

Let X denote an arbitrarily given set. The members of X will be called *points*.

By a *topology* in X, we mean a nonempty collection τ of subsets, which will be called *open sets*, satisfying the following four axioms:

(OS1) *The empty set $\square$ is open.*
(OS2) *The set X itself is open.*
(OS3) *The union of any family of open sets is open.*
(OS4) *The intersection of any two (and hence of any finite number of) open sets is open.*

A set X is said to be *topologized* if a topology τ has been given in X. A topologized set X will be called a *topological space* or simply a *space* and the topology τ in X is called *the topology of the space X*. The members of τ will be called the *open sets of the space X*.

EXAMPLES OF TOPOLOGICAL SPACES

(1) *Discrete spaces.* Let X be any set. The collection of *all* subsets of X obviously satisfies the axioms for open sets and hence is a topology in X which is called the *discrete topology* in X. If X is topologized by its discrete topology, it is called a *discrete space*.

(2) *Indiscrete spaces.* Let X be any set. The collection $\{\square, X\}$ satisfies the axioms for open sets and hence is a topology in X which is called the *indiscrete* (or *trivial*) *topology* in X. If X is topologized by its indiscrete topology, it is called an *indiscrete space*.

(3) *Metric spaces.* Let X be any metric space with metric $d : X^2 \to R$. By (1.3), the open sets of X defined in §1 constitute a topology in X which is called the *topology defined by the metric d* or the *topology of the metric space* X. Hence metric spaces are special cases of topological spaces.

Since topologies in a set X are special collections of subsets of X, we can compare topologies in the same set X by means of the inclusion relation. Let σ and τ be any two topologies in X. If $\sigma \subset \tau$, then we shall say that σ is *smaller* than τ and τ is *larger* than σ. It is also said that σ is *coarser* than τ and τ is *finer* than σ. Unfortunately, the more familiar terms "stronger" and "weaker" are used in contradictory senses in algebraic topology and functional analysis: If $\sigma \subset \tau$, in algebraic topology σ is said to be stronger than τ, while in functional analysis σ is said to be weaker than τ. On the other hand, τ is said to be weaker than σ in algebraic topology and τ is said to be stronger than σ in functional analysis.

By a *basis* of a topology τ in X, we mean a subcollection β of τ such that every open set U in τ is a union of some open sets in β. In other words, a subcollection β of τ is a basis of τ iff, for every $U \epsilon \tau$ and each $x \epsilon U$, there is a $V \epsilon \beta$ such that

$$x \epsilon V \subset U.$$

The open sets of a given basis β will be called the *basic open sets* of the space X.

According to (1.4) and (1.5), the open balls $B_\delta(p)$ of a metric space X for all points $p \epsilon X$ and all positive real numbers δ form a basis of the topology τ of the metric space X. In particular, the open intervals of the real line R form a basis of the topology τ in R defined by the metric given in the example (1) of §1.

Let X be a given space with topology τ and let p denote an arbitrary point in X. A set $N \subset X$ is said to be a *neighborhood* of the point p in the space X iff there exists an open set U of X satisfying

$$p \epsilon U \subset N.$$

Hence a neighborhood of a point p in a space X is a set in X containing not only the point p itself but also some open set of X which contains p.

For an arbitrarily given point p in a space X, the family of all neighborhoods of p in X will be called the *neighborhood system* of the point p in the space X.

By a *local basis*, or a *neighborhood basis*, of a space X at a point $p \epsilon X$, we mean a collection β of neighborhoods of p in X such that every neighborhood of p in X contains a member of β. The members of a given local basis β of X at a point $p \epsilon X$ will be called the *basic neighborhoods* of p in X.

For example, let X be a metric space. Then, for any given point p of X, the open balls $B_\delta(p)$ of X for all positive real numbers δ obviously constitute a local basis of X at the point p.

A space X is said to satisfy the *first axiom of countability* iff it has a countable local basis at each of its points. As an example, we have the following proposition.

PROPOSITION 4.1. *Every metric space satisfies the first axiom of countability.*

Proof. Let X denote an arbitrary metric space and p be any point in X. Let

$$\{\delta_1, \delta_2, \ldots, \delta_n, \ldots\}$$

denote any sequence of positive real numbers converging to zero. It remains to prove that the collection

$$\beta = \{N_{\delta_i}(p) \mid i = 1, 2, \ldots\}$$

is a local basis of X at the point p. For this purpose, let N be any given neighborhood of p in X. By definition, there exists a positive real number δ such that

$$N_\delta(p) \subset N.$$

Since the sequence $\{\delta_1, \delta_2, \ldots, \delta_n, \ldots\}$ converges to zero, there exists a natural number n with $\delta_n \leqslant \delta$. This implies

$$p \, \epsilon \, N_{\delta_n}(p) \subset N.$$

Hence β is a local basis of X at p.$\|$

A space X is said to satisfy the *second axiom of countability* iff its topology τ has a countable basis.

PROPOSITION 4.2. *If a space X satisfies the second axiom of countability, then it satisfies also the first axiom of countability.*

Proof. Since X satisfies the second axiom of countability, its topology τ has a countable basis β. To prove that X satisfies the first axiom of countability, let p denote an arbitrary point of X. Let

$$\lambda = \{U \, \epsilon \, \beta \mid p \, \epsilon \, U\}.$$

Then every member of λ is a neighborhood of p in X. As a subcollection of a countable collection β, λ is countable. It remains to prove that λ is a local basis of X at the point p. For this purpose, let N denote any neighborhood of p in X. By definition, there exists an open set W of X satisfying

$$p \, \epsilon \, W \subset N.$$

Since β is a basis of τ and W is open, there exists a basic open set $U \, \epsilon \, \beta$ satisfying

$$p \, \epsilon \, U \subset W.$$

This implies $U \, \epsilon \, \lambda$ and $U \subset N$. Hence λ is a local basis of X at p.$\|$

The converse of (4.2) is false. In fact, every discrete space X satisfies the first axiom of countability, but X does not satisfy the second axiom of countability unless X itself is countable.

By using neighborhoods instead of the open balls, it is not difficult to generalize the notions introduced in §1 for metric spaces to topological spaces. For example, consider an arbitrary set E in any given topological space X.

A point p of X is said to be an *interior point* of the set E iff there exists a neighborhood N of p in X with $N \subset E$. A point p of X is said to be an *exterior point* of E iff there exists a neighborhood N of p in X with $N \subset X \backslash E$. Finally, a point p of X is said to be a *boundary point*, or *frontier point*, of E iff every neighborhood N of p in X contains at least one point in E and at least one point not in E.

Then the *interior* $\mathrm{Int}(E)$, the *exterior* $\mathrm{Ext}(E)$, and the *boundary* $\partial(E)$ of E in X are defined in precisely the same way as in §1. Besides, we define the *closure* $\mathrm{Cl}(E)$ of E by

$$\mathrm{Cl}(E) = E \cup \partial(E)$$

and that E is said to be *closed* iff $\partial(E) \subset E$, or equivalently $\mathrm{Cl}(E) = E$, holds.

Having generalized these notions to topological spaces, one can verify that the assertions (1.6)–(1.12) are still true.

Now let us generalize the notion of continuity to functions on topological spaces.

For this purpose, let us consider a function

$$f : X \to Y$$

of which both the domain X and the range Y are topological spaces. The function f is said to be *continuous at a point p* of X iff, for every neighborhood N of the point $f(p)$ in Y, there exists a neighborhood M of the point p in X satisfying

$$f(M) \subset N.$$

The function f is said to be *continuous* iff it is continuous at every point of X. Continuous functions are called *mappings* or *maps*.

For example, the constant functions from a space X into a space Y are continuous and will be called the *constant maps*. As another example, the identity function on a space X is continuous and will be called the *identity map* on X.

One can easily verify that (3.6) holds also for any function $f : X \to Y$ from a topological space X into a topological space Y.

A function $f : X \to Y$ from a space X into a space Y is said to be *open* iff the image $f(U)$ of every open set U in X is open in Y. Similarly, $f:X \rightarrow Y$ is said to be *closed* iff the image $f(F)$ of every closed set F in X is closed in Y.

If a map $f:X \rightarrow Y$ is bijective, then its inverse function

$$f^{-1}:Y \rightarrow X$$

is well-defined but not always continuous. For example, let X denote the space of all real numbers with discrete topology and Y denote the real line. Then the identity function $i:X \rightarrow Y$ is a bijective map, but its inverse function $i^{-1}:Y \rightarrow X$ fails to be continuous.

As to the continuity of the inverse function of a bijective map, the following proposition is obvious.

PROPOSITION 4.3. *For any bijective map* $f:X \rightarrow Y$, *the following three statements are equivalent.*

(**a**) *The inverse function* $f^{-1}:Y \rightarrow X$ *is continuous.*
(**b**) $f:X \rightarrow Y$ *is open.*
(**c**) $f:X \rightarrow Y$ *is closed.*

By a *homeomorphism*, or *topological map*, we mean a bijective map

$$f:X \rightarrow Y$$

which satisfies the equivalent conditions (**a**), (**b**), (**c**) in (4.3). If a homeomorphism $f:X \rightarrow Y$ exists, then the two spaces X and Y are said to be *homeomorphic*, or *topologically equivalent*, and each space is said to be a *homeomorph* of the other.

A property which when possessed by a space is also possessed by each of its homeomorphs is called a *topological property*. Formally, *topology* is the branch of mathematics which studies topological properties of spaces. In the remainder of this final section, we will study a few topological properties of spaces.

By a *Hausdorff space*, we mean a space X which satisfies the following *Hausdorff separation axiom:* Every two distinct points of X have disjoint neighborhoods in X; in other words, if a and b are distinct points of X, then there exist open sets U and V in X, satisfying

$$a \in U, \qquad b \in V, \qquad U \cap V = \square.$$

For example, every metric space is a Hausdorff space. Every discrete space clearly satisfies the Hausdorff separation axiom, while an indiscrete space with more than one point can never be a Hausdorff space.

To establish an interesting property of Hausdorff spaces, let us introduce the notion of retracts. A subset E of a space X is said to be a *retract* of X iff there exists a map

$$r:X \to X$$

satisfying $r(x) \in E$ for every $x \in X$ and $r(e) = e$ for every $e \in E$. Such a map r is called a *retraction of X onto E*.

PROPOSITION 4.4. *If E is a retract of a Hausdorff space X, then E is a closed set in X.*

Proof. Assume that E is a retract of a Hausdorff space X. Then there is a retraction r of X onto E. We are going to prove that $X \backslash E$ is an open set in X.

If $X \backslash E = \square$, the proposition is trivial. Thus, we assume $X \backslash E \neq \square$. Let a denote an arbitrary point in $X \backslash E$. Then the point $b = r(a)$ is in E and hence we have $a \neq b$. Since X is a Hausdorff space, there exist open sets U and V of X satisfying

$$a \in U, \qquad b \in V, \qquad U \cap V = \square.$$

Since $r:X \to X$ is continuous and V is open, it follows from (3.6) that $f^{-1}(V)$ is an open set of X containing the point a. Let

$$W = U \cap f^{-1}(V).$$

Then W is an open set of X satisfying

$$a \in W, \qquad V \cap W = \square, \qquad r(W) \subset V. \qquad \qquad \textbf{.}$$

This implies that $r(x) \neq x$ for every $x \in W$ and hence $W \subset X \backslash E$. Since a is an arbitrary point of $X \backslash E$, this implies that $X \backslash E$ is open and, therefore, E is closed. ‖

Since constant functions are continuous, it follows that, for every point p of a space X, the set $\{p\}$ is a retract of X. Therefore, (4.4) implies that a Hausdorff space X has the following property: *Every point of X forms a closed set in X.* A space X which has this property is called a *Fréchet space* or a *T_1-space*. It follows immediately that every Fréchet space X satisfies the following *Fréchet separation axiom:* For any pair of distinct points a and b in X, there exists an open set U of X such that $a \in U$ and $b \notin U$.

A space X is said to be *regular at a point p* of X iff every neighborhood of p contains a closed neighborhood of p. By a *regular space*, we mean a space X which is regular at each of its points. For example, metric spaces and discrete spaces are regular.

PROPOSITION 4.5. *Every regular Fréchet space is a Hausdorff space.*

Proof. Let X be a regular Fréchet space and let a, b denote any two distinct points in X. Since X is a Fréchet space, $X \setminus \{b\}$ is an open set of X. From the regularity of X at the point a, there follows the existence of a closed neighborhood N of a with $N \subset X \setminus \{b\}$. Let

$$U = \text{Int}(N), \qquad V = X \setminus N.$$

Then U and V are open sets of X with $a \in U$, $b \in V$, and $U \cap V = \square$. This proves that X is a Hausdorff space.$\|$

For more topological properties of spaces, the interested student is referred to either of the author's books on general topology mentioned in the introductory paragraph of this chapter.

EXERCISES

4A. Prove that a set U of a space X is open iff U is a neighborhood of each of its points.

4B. By a *filter* of subsets of a set X, we mean a collection $\mathfrak{F}$ of subsets of X satisfying the following two conditions:

    (a) Each subset of X which contains a member of $\mathfrak{F}$ belongs to $\mathfrak{F}$.
    (b) The intersection of any finite number of members of $\mathfrak{F}$ belongs to $\mathfrak{F}$.

Prove that the neighborhood system of a point p in a space X is a filter of subsets of X.

4C. Let X, Y, Z be spaces and consider functions

$$X \xrightarrow{\;f\;} Y \xrightarrow{\;g\;} Z.$$

Prove the following two assertions:
    (a) If f and g are continuous, so is the composition $g \circ f$.
    (b) If f and g are homeomorphisms, then f^{-1}, g^{-1}, and $g \circ f$ are also homeomorphisms.

INDEX